MENTAL ILLNESS

MENTAL ILLNESS

A GUIDE FOR THE FAMILY

Fifth Edition

by EDITH M. STERN

Foreword by William C. Menninger, M.D.

HARPER & ROW, PUBLISHERS

NEW YORK AND EVANSTON

*To the thousands of anxious men and women
who have mentally ill relatives, in the hope
that they will find in these pages some comfort
and practical guidance*

Contents

Acknowledgments

To THE MANY AUTHORITIES who contributed to the currency and accuracy of this 1967 edition I am deeply grateful.

Walter E. Barton, M.D., Medical Director, American Psychiatric Association; Lucy D. Ozarin, M.D., Psychiatrist, National Institute of Mental Health; William F. Sheeley, M.D., Commissioner of Mental Health, Indiana; and Joseph Kadish, Ph.D., Health Adviser, United States Public Health Service, made preliminary suggestions for changes from the 1962 publication; later, Drs. Barton and Ozarin, in addition, reviewed the manuscript.

Eugene M. Caffey, Jr., M.D., Assistant Chief, Psychiatry Division, Psychiatry, Neurology, and Psychology Service, Veterans Administration Central Office, reviewed the manuscript for references to the Veterans Administration. Melvin Herman, Executive Secretary, National Association of Private Psychiatric Hospitals, read the sections pertaining to public and private hospitals in the 1962 edition and recommended changes. Henry Weihofen, Professor of Law, University of New Mexico, Honorary Fellow, American Psychiatric Association, was my primary guide for alterations involving legalities. Zigmond Lebensohn, M.D., Chief, Department of Psychiatry, Sibley Memorial Hospital, Washington, D.C., Chairman, Committee on Psychiatry and Law, Group for the Advancement of Psychiatry, also reviewed and approved legal sections. I am indebted to him besides for taking me through a general hospital's psychiatric service for private patients, and for assistance in the updating of the section on electrotherapy. James L. Anderson, M.D., Miami, Florida, was similarly helpful about electrotherapy.

John D. Schultz, M.D., Assistant Director for Mental Health and Retardation, District of Columbia Department of Public Health, furthered my study and inspection of a psychiatric service for those who are not private patients, in governmentally supported D.C. General Hospital, and he explained and threw open to me the D.C. Community Mental Health Center. Ralph Meng, M.D., Bethesda, Maryland, steered me to another kind of community mental health center developed at Eastern Shore State Hospital, Maryland. The hospitality and helpfulness of its superintendent, Harold English, M.D., increased my understanding of the community role a state hospital can have.

Raymond M. Glasscote, Chief, Joint Information Service, National Association for Mental Health and American Psychiatric Association, supplied numerous facts. Mrs. Ruth J. Knee, Chief, Mental Health Care, Administration Branch, National Institute of Mental Health, authenticated what federal funds might be available for mental patients. Bernard Posner, Deputy Secretary, The President's Committee on Employment of the Handicapped, not only advised on and checked material pertaining to vocational rehabilitation and employment of the mentally ill, but also, along with Robert L. Robinson, Information Officer, American Psychiatric Association, helped me resolve doubts as to wording in various parts of the manuscript.

Finally, I want to thank those Executive Directors of Mental Health Associations who shared their knowledge of the questions families ask.

EDITH M. STERN

Washington, D.C.

Foreword to
the Fourth Edition

FOR THE LAST THIRTY YEARS my full time has been devoted to consulting and counseling with troubled people—mentally ill patients. Many of these have required hospitalization. Very rarely in all of these years have I seen a family who was not greatly distressed, usually somewhat mystified, almost always perplexed, and far too often totally unprepared to cope with the ordeal. Probably no family ever will face this crisis with equanimity, but the distress and mystery and lack of information which are almost always present can be greatly reduced, not only to the patient's great benefit but also with immense relief to the family.

Edith Stern's book aims to do just that. It is a simple and practical explanation of the problems confronting the relatives of the mentally ill patient. In a very sympathetic manner and with rare acumen in anticipating questions, Mrs. Stern attempts to clear the uncertainty and give helpful information to troubled relatives. I know of no other document that begins to approach this presentation in its helpfulness and its thoroughness. My guess is that the relative who finds it is indeed fortunate and will read and reread it. It begins with a simple, rational explanation of mental illness. It follows the relative through the experiences of admis-

11

sion and treatment in the hospital, and concludes with suggestions about the patient's homecoming.

This book even goes much further—if it were to be so used —than merely being of help to a relative of a mentally ill patient. It is a treatise on the understanding of the mental ill- nesses which require hospitalization. It would be worthwhile reading for any layman who wants to understand this subject more adequately—and so much misunderstanding does prevail.

Edith Stern has made a wonderfully helpful contribution to this badly neglected field of mental illness. If and when mental illness strikes, as it does in so many instances, most families blunder along, often never fully understanding the patient and his illness or their role. This book can be invaluable to them. Would that the relatives of every mentally ill patient could have the advantage—and the comfort—of the information presented in this book—preferably before the mental illness strikes, but certainly just as soon afterward as possible. I am sure that it would save them much uncertainty and anguish.

WILLIAM C. MENNINGER, M.D.

MENTAL ILLNESS

CHAPTER 1

A Healthy Attitude Toward Mental Illness

SOMETIME DURING HIS LIFETIME some member of nearly every family behaves so abnormally that he needs help from people especially trained to give it. This may be anything from knowledgeable dealing with a single telephone call to treatment in a mental hospital. Mental illnesses, like other illnesses, range from very mild to severe.

Yet almost every time mental illness strikes in any form, there is much unnecessary suffering for both relatives and patient, because however much we may have read on the subject most of us are unprepared when anyone we love ceases to be himself. His very closeness may have made us unaware of small, gradual changes in his attitudes, ideas, and personality. Many of us, also, are unfamiliar with the medical resources for restoring someone to normality, and of the way community mental health centers, clinics, and hospitals are set up to help a mental patient get well.

The most important thing for your relative's chances of recovery—and for your own peace of mind—is to realize that mental illnesses are illnesses, different from others, to be sure, but still illnesses.

15

In other kinds of illnesses there are likely to be pain and weakness and most patients want to be helped. In mental illnesses the patients are often not appealing, and often reject help. If you are angry or disgusted with your relative, you are having reactions common in families of the mentally ill. No matter how much you may love someone, it is only natural to become anything from annoyed to furious if he has been disrupting your family life, wrecking your finances, tearing your heart, avoiding responsibility, or staying provokingly aloof from anyone who tries to be loving or friendly.

Once you can accept the fact that you are dealing with someone who is sick, however, you will be less exasperated and anguished by the incomprehensibly perverse and unreasonable actions of the sufferer. You will no more think of blaming him for the torrent of abuse he pours forth upon you, for his "stubbornness," his dirty habits, his destructiveness, or the "lazy" way he sits staring for hours instead of going about his business than you would blame him for vomiting if he had stomach trouble, or for lying idle if he had a broken back. Moral censure, exasperated wonderings of "Why *must* he behave like that?" will give way to a kind of sympathy you would naturally give anyone physically incapacitated. Both physical and mental breakdowns are misfortunes. But the one nearly always comes as a heavier blow than the other and can be more devastating to family life, because along with it go changes in personality. The person you love seems to have become someone else, unreasonable and unreachable.

In mental illness especially, the attitudes of relatives play a large part, for better or for worse. Therefore your patient's chances for recovery will be markedly increased if you look upon him as ill instead of well but ornery.

You will, also, spare yourself much self-torture and also help speed your relative along the road to mental health if you realize that, although mental illness is still too often viewed as a disgrace, actually no more stigma should be attached to a disordered mind than to a disordered digestion or circulation. The sheer facts of the disorder are hard enough to bear. Do not complicate and magnify them for all concerned by delaying to call in help because of false shame.

Bear in mind, also, that it does not mean your family is "tainted" because one of its members has a mental breakdown. Some mental diseases have virtually nothing to do with heredity. Students differ on the hereditary nature of others.

Indeed, although there may have been several cases of mental illness in the family, the present one might very well be the last. Even where heredity sets the stage for a mental disease, it does not necessarily appear. A person's life history may have much more to do with his mental and emotional condition than does his family history. So if someone with a hereditary predisposition to a mental disorder does not have shattering experiences, he can be mentally healthy all his life.

Therefore, because you have one or more mentally ill relatives, it does not follow that all the rest of you are doomed. Face the truth of your relative's condition frankly. Do not shut your eyes to it by maintaining, "there's really nothing wrong with him," or "he's just acting up"; but do not aggravate the upheaval and sorrow, which come inevitably with any illness, with dire speculations about your grandparents and your grandchildren, or with anxious observation of your other relatives. If someone in your family had to be hospitalized for diabetes, you wouldn't begin agonizing every time anyone else took a piece of sugar, even though you might justifiably suspect that a tendency to diabetes was hereditary.

To say, when mental illness strikes, that "there's nothing either good or bad but thinking makes it so," would be unwarranted glossing over the realities of the situation. It is certainly a misfortune. But it need not inevitably become tragedy if you have a wholesome, realistic acceptance of abnormal behavior for exactly what it is—a sickness to which some individuals are subject and to which modern medical science has found many of the answers.

CHAPTER 2

When Mental Illness Strikes

MEDICAL HELP is as necessary for recognizing the symptoms of mental disorders as for recognizing the symptoms of physical disorders. Most of us have no conception of mental illness because we have had no direct experience with it. If you have ever seen a convulsion, you have some idea of how wrong things can go with the brain that controls the nervous system; if you have had experience with heavy drinkers, you have encountered drastic alterations of everyday behavior. Probably you know someone in the community who stands out as "peculiar"; or perhaps one of your friends has "gone to pieces" or has had a nervous breakdown. But even familiarity with all of these doesn't mean you can recognize even a serious mental illness in someone dear to you. Since your emotions quite naturally color your reason, you cannot easily bring yourself to admit what would be obvious to an expert and suspicious to everyone else.

Mental illness takes on many different forms. Its victim may be unable to accomplish anything. He may be silent, listless, and depressed. He may be very much excited and talk continuously, leaping from one idea to another. He may endlessly repeat acts

19

such as washing his hands or touching certain objects. He may act bafflingly aloof from others. He may have fixed ideas, which no reasoning or proof to the contrary can remove—anything from the notion that his food is poisoned to the conviction that it is his mission to save the world. He may be cripplingly tense and uneasy about vague, anticipated dangers. He may have hallucinations, that is, see or hear what does not really exist. He may, in short, do anything exaggerated or outlandish.

Because of this wide variety in behavior, because mental breakdown often comes on slowly and insidiously, because we love our relatives and catch at straws to convince ourselves that they are all right, because we feel ashamed, too many of us let mental illness go untreated much longer than we should and thereby invite disaster. Doctors agree that the sooner they are called in on a case, the better the chances for recovery. When someone in your family does not behave normally, confer with your family physician, just as you would if temperature, appetite, or skin condition were not normal.

This doesn't mean that you should become alarmed every time a member of your household does something erratic or peculiar. But it does mean that you should use the same common sense as in physical illness. When a person is incapacitated for work because he has flu or a broken arm, or when he might be a danger to the community because of a possible infectious disease, you consult the doctor. Similarly, consult the doctor when anyone cannot carry on his daily business because he is beginning to brood, or is flying from one thing to another, or is obsessed with certain fixed ideas not supported by the facts, making sinister interpretations of people's simplest actions or giving mistaken explanations of everyday occurrences; if he acts unusually silly, grinning and laughing without apparent cause; if he hears "voices" that tell him what to do; if he breaks frugal habits of a lifetime, going on spending sprees and buying expensive articles for which he cannot pay, or if he has become an alcoholic; if he tears himself down by continually talking about how sinful or what a failure he is; if, besides having the usual physical infirmities of old age, he is so extremely confused and forgetful that he cannot look after himself safely; if he might become a danger to the community because he is driving recklessly or tearing down your neighbor's fence or throwing stones at windows. In brief, consult the doctor whenever his behavior is seriously different from what it has been. /

If you are unable to reach your doctor in an emergency, or have no regular family physician, find out from the local Mental Health Association or the Health Department what you can do. You may be so fortunate as to live in a community that has some kind of psychiatric emergency service. It may be connected with a general hospital, a private or public mental hospital, or a mental health center. In a handful of communities an emergency mental health team will come to your home. Some emergency services have psychiatrists on call; some have walk-in clinics. In others there is twenty-four-hour emergency telephone service where calls are answered by a specially trained staff. Often, merely with their skilled replies, they can tide troubled callers or their relatives over a crisis without referral to a psychiatrist or clinic.

The poor, for example, are subject to disturbance and depression because of overwhelming practical problems. The mother of seven children may be suddenly deserted, with no food in the house and no money to buy any; or a family may be evicted. When such telephone callers are calmed and told just where to get financial help, symptoms may shortly disappear.

One of the most serious emergencies, of course, is attempted suicide. There are some special suicide-prevention centers that do much more for the patient than—as is all too common at general hospital emergency rooms—just patch him up physically and send him home. These centers either help would-be suicides to understand themselves or steer them to those who can give such help. Never take even an indirect threat of suicide lightly, but recognize it as a cry for help. Do not gamble with your relative's life by taking it solely upon yourself to protect his life. Not everyone can gauge by behavior when special precautions should be taken. Some persons with suicidal intent talk about committing suicide; some do not. Some try to kill themselves when they are the most depressed; some, when they appear extraordinarily cheerful and alert. Both those who have unsuccessfully attempted suicide and those who still only talk about it need skilled services.

If a doctor, after he has made his examination, diagnoses some kind of mental illness, believe what he says against all your hopes, wishes, and convictions that it can't possibly be so. True, doctors do not know everything, but they do have the training and experience that qualify them to be our best authorities on the health of body and mind, and at least they know more about this than the rest of us.

The doctor may decide he can treat the patient himself, or he may want to call in a psychiatrist, a doctor of medicine with special training and experience in the field of emotional illness and mental disorders. He takes physical as well as psychological factors into account, and is as well equipped to deal with mental disorders as a pediatrician is to deal with the disorders of childhood.

You might have the problem of a relative who is so sure there is nothing wrong with him that he refuses to see a psychiatrist or any other doctor. This kind of roadblock cannot be battered down by threats, arguments, or insistence, so try another road to help. Unless your relative is completely irrational and uncontrollable, suggest that he have a talk with his minister, priest, or rabbi. A number of clergymen have had special training in the relation between religion and psychiatry, which despite different approaches have as a common goal peace within one's self. Such "clinically" trained clergymen know not only how to counsel someone mentally ill, but also when and how to induce him to consult a psychiatrist. Many other individual clergymen, too, are helpful with mental health problems. Moreover, they are the only professionals free to come in unasked.

Some communities have a "pastoral counseling service" or "pastoral institute." It may be denominationally sponsored, or interdenominational, but usually it is open to anyone paying a quite modest fee in accordance with his means. Such services, although rendered by mental-health-minded clergymen, work in cooperation with psychiatrists, or have a consultant psychiatrist on the staff. Your local Mental Health Association knows whether your community has an organized pastoral counseling service.

Family Service agencies are another resource. There are over two hundred of these in the United States, and you can locate the one nearest you from the telephone directory (perhaps with Protestant, Catholic, Jewish, or Community as the first word of the title), through the Mental Health Association, or by writing to the Family Service Association of America, 44 East 23rd Street, New York, New York 10010. Ask your relative, for the family's sake, or yours—anything but his own—to consult a Family Service agency about his troubles so that you can all live more happily together again. Tell him that perhaps he can find out how to deal more comfortably with the rest of you. Thus, you will not aggravate his conviction that he is right and everybody else is wrong; moreover, the word "family" is less likely to inflame him than "psychiatrist" or "mental health."

The social workers who staff Family Service agencies, like clinically trained clergymen, know when a mental or emotional disorder can be corrected with counseling, and when it cannot and a psychiatrist is needed; so when advisable they will use their skills to guide your relative to a psychiatrist or psychiatric clinic. As with pastoral counseling services, modest fees are adjusted to means.

Probably you yourself will feel a great need to talk over your problems with someone besides the doctors. Community pastoral or Family Service counseling agencies can be as helpful to you as to your relative. In fact, you might find it a very good idea to make an appointment so that you can unburden yourself before, during, or after your relative's counseling at one of these agencies.

In any case, do not take the advice of well-meaning but uninformed friends at this or at any other stage of your involvement with mental illness. Perhaps they will assure you soothingly that all your relative needs is a change or a rest. They may try to console you with terms like "high-strung," "nervous breakdown," "run-down," or "upset"—which are scientifically meaningless. They may declare that if you follow their recommendations of this or that diet, method of recreation or exercise, "he'll soon be himself again."

Amateur remedies for mental illness are more numerous than amateur remedies for colds, and far less harmless. For instance, a visit away from home may plunge a depressed patient into even greater gloom because he feels strange and lonely. Because you know or a friend knows someone who has been benefited by going on a cruise, that does not mean that the same treatment is good for your mental invalid: he may jump into the water. Lay advisers, with the kindliest intentions, may urge rest when exercise is needed, or exercise instead of beneficial rest.

Or perhaps your friends will recommend disciplinary measures. With sympathy for you, they may describe your patient as "impossible," "vicious," "stubborn," "just plain mean," or in any other derogatory terms, and advise you to "tell him where to get off," to "clear out," or to "put him out." To follow such counsel would be like condemning your relative because he is crippled, or abandoning him because he has heart trouble.

Particularly trying to everyone with whom they come in contact are those mentally ill persons not at all confused—indeed very logical if we could accept their premises—who are sure they are badly treated, sometimes by the world in general, sometimes by local groups like the women's club or the church or the lodge, but most often by those close to them through ties of blood or marriage. Persons so afflicted tell remarkably credible stories about their abuses; often in their attempt to right them they manage to enlist help from friends. They make life miserable for others by acting upon their beliefs of being ill-used; they slander their neighbors, interfere in their husband's business, and meddle in their children's affairs. If they hold responsible positions and continue with their work, they may do much harm by using poor judgment or being unjust to others. During the gradual growth of their disorder we think of them as disagreeable and malicious and wish fervently that they would mend their ways. The earlier, however, that such tendencies are recognized as symptoms of mental illness, the fewer practical and emotional complications there are for the families concerned, and the most favorable prospects for cure. Disregard any suggestions from your friends about "lawsuits," or "reform," or "a good lesson," or "making her see the light." To straighten out such behavior you want not a policeman or a lawyer or, as any experienced clergyman will tell you, a minister. What you need is a doctor.

Although to a distraught family abnormal behavior seems to follow no rhyme or reason and appears unpredictable, unique, and terrifying, psychiatrists know that most forms of mental illness follow definite patterns, well recognized and classified.

More often than many despairing families realize, too, in the face of failure brought on by their own delays and mistakes, mental illness, especially when it is brought to medical attention early enough, can be successfully treated right in the community.

CHAPTER *3*

Keeping the Patient in the Community

THE COMMUNITY may be anything from an immediate neighborhood in a large city to a sparsely settled county or group of counties. But city, town, or rural area, it is where your relative lives, works, or goes to school, and where he has his friends and family. It is also where the great majority of mental patients can and should be treated.

Face it frankly, however, and without guilt: keeping your relative there, and perhaps in your home, may not be what you would prefer. He has certainly not been easy to live with, and it might be a great relief to get him out of your hair, at least temporarily, at an agreeable, restful distance. But although it is quite natural for you to feel this way, realize that the decision on the required treatment must be made professionally by others not involved. They will want to keep him near by if that is at all possible. It is as hard on a mental patient as it would be on anyone else to be ripped away from everything and everyone familiar and to be put among strangers in the strange surroundings of a perhaps-distant hospital. In many cases the very interruption to ordinary living causes a setback.

You will find many valuable suggestions in the pamphlet *Helping a Mental Patient at Home* (15 cents, available from your local or state Mental Health Association). But no matter how wisely and well you manage with your relative at home, whether or not he can be treated in the community depends to a large extent on what mental health services it affords.

If a family physician or private-practice psychiatrist is caring for your relative, do not go shopping for local facilities. He will know about these, so be guided by his recommendations. Incidentally, before you decide that you cannot afford a private doctor be sure to check the provisions in your relative's health insurance. During the past few years most insurance policies, including Medicare, have begun to include psychiatric with other kinds of coverable medical costs.

Even if you cannot have a private-practice physician, you may be so fortunate as to live in a community that has a publicly or privately supported mental health center. There are already several hundred such centers and their number is rapidly increasing. A community mental health center may be in a brand-new building or group of buildings especially built for the purpose, but not necessarily so. It may be simply a wing added to a general hospital, an old building converted to an outpatient clinic, or scattered buildings, new and old, put to various mental health uses. The heart of a good community mental health center is not a place but a program. The goals are to see that services are coordinated, that the patient gets the treatment he needs at the time he needs it, that as his condition changes he is moved easily from one kind of facility and treatment to another, and that he gets consistent and continuous professional care from the first cry for help until he no longer needs it. The goals are not always achieved. Although community mental health centers have been greatly stimulated since 1963 by federal funds, they are still so new that many have lacks and gaps. Probably the greatest are in services to old people and to children.

But even if your own community lacks a comprehensive mental health center, or has none at all, this does not mean it has no resources for helping your relative to stay in it.

Outpatient clinics are numerous. "Outpatient" means that the patient lives at home, carries on his daily business if possible, and goes to the clinic by appointment one or more times a week, just as he would go to the office of a private psychiatrist. The clinic may be connected with a general hospital or a Veterans Administration hospital, or it may be operated by a local community group. A disadvantage of many clinics is that they have long waiting lists. But then many private-practice doctors are so booked up that a new patient, no matter what he can pay, may also have a long wait for his first appointment.

Over one thousand general hospitals, among some six thousand in the United States, are assuming the responsibility for mental ills that general hospitals have traditionally assumed for physical ills. About half of these have special psychiatric "units" or "wards" or "services." The other half care for psychiatric patients among others. But the number of general hospitals accepting the mentally ill actually represents much less than the number of beds available. This is because practically all the large municipal hospitals in the greatest centers of population have psychiatric services. Not only are many more mental patients today being treated in community general hospitals than in state or private residential mental hospitals, but also turnover is greater.

In a few tax-supported general hospitals, unhappily, the psychiatric service is little more than a way station to the state hospital. But from general hospitals as a whole, some 90 per cent of all patients go directly back to their homes and families, over half of them within a few days or weeks.

University-connected hospitals tend to give preference to patients suitable for teaching purposes. If your relative is one of them, rejoice, rather than fear he will be "used as a guinea pig."

Teaching hospitals are usually excellent, with the patients getting a great deal of up-to-date, skilled, intelligent attention.

Most, although not all, of the privately supported, or "voluntary" general, hospitals accept only private patients who have their own psychiatrists. The daily cost is high, but the stay is likely to be brief. Here again, check your relative's health insurance policy to find out whether it covers hospitalization for mental illness. There are obvious advantages in continuing with the same doctor with whom one began.

In some localities the Medicaid program of the welfare department may help pay the costs of a mental patient's short stay in a general hospital. If your relative has no insurance and not enough money to pay his own way, before you assume that he will have to go to a state hospital outside the community (for which all states will pay wholly or in part) inquire at the local general hospital or welfare department if he can be admitted under such a plan. For patients over sixty-five, the Medicare program will pay on the same terms for psychiatric illness as for any other illness requiring hospitalization.

For needy older persons unable to manage their own funds, Social Security provides for "protective payments" to a third person on their behalf. Though this arrangement does not directly cover hospitalization, it may enable a family to keep a confused aged parent in his own home or theirs.

Admission of a mental patient to a community general hospital is the same as admission of any other kind of patient. A medical decision is the only one necessary; there are no legal proceedings. The patient is free to leave whenever he wishes. Naturally, if the hospital does not consider him well enough to go, his doctor will try to persuade him to remain for a while. Where such persuasion is unsuccessful, the patient may have to sign a statement that he is leaving against medical advice, but this is just between him and the hospital, with no court involved.

Most psychiatric wards in general hospitals are "open," that is, without locked doors. All of this bona fide sense of freedom of choice is obviously good for someone who has been feeling put upon, persecuted, or abused. It is also good for the family, who otherwise might feel guilty for sending the patient out of the community, compelling him to be hospitalized by court order, or detaining him in a hospital against his will.

Both general hospitals and mental hospitals more and more make arrangements for part-time hospitalization. There is a variety of plans whereby patients do not live in the hospital twenty-four hours a day, seven days a week. Day and half-day hospital patients have treatments and activities similar to what they would have in a full-time mental hospital, but return home every afternoon or night. Night hospital patients work in the community during the day, then get afterhours treatment and sleep at the hospital. There are even weekend arrangements. The patient may stay at the hospital all week, but go home on weekends. Or, conversely, he may live at home and go to his job during the workweek, then get treatment and stay at the hospital on Saturdays and Sundays.

Sometimes a state Vocational Rehabilitation Agency teaches new skills or gives refresher courses in old ones to patients hospitalized part-time or attending outpatient clinics. Under certain circumstances it may pay for the psychiatric treatment.

If a patient regularly returns to his part-time hospital more difficult and disturbed from having been at home, staff members carefully reconsider the advantages of part-time hospitalization against the disadvantages. In many cases, despite temporary setbacks, the very fact that patients must go back and face the realities of where and with whom they live is beneficial. Because modern psychiatry attempts to build up the well part of a person without emphasis on the part that is sick, giving him even the part-time responsibility for getting along in the community, in his home, and on the job may be the firm foundation for resuming responsibility full-time.

The family has a responsibility too. Unless it is sympathetic, tolerant, and cooperative, community methods will not work. If your relative is supposed to take pills, be sure he takes them. By your actions and attitudes, as well as by words, make him feel that he is an inseparable, important part of the household and family group. Disagreeable or remote though he may be during the time he spends with you, do your best to take his provoking behavior or long silences in your stride. Bear in mind that his going back and forth from the hospital are part of the treatment that may prevent his ever having to be hospitalized full-time.

But often part-time hospitalization has advantages for the family, too. Take, for instance, the case of a confused or disturbed aged mother who requires such constant attention that the woman of the household is unable to take a much-needed job. Care and treatment for a while at a good day hospital not only relieves the situation but also may improve the patient's condition to the point where she is no longer a problem. At the same time, she is spared the pain of feeling rejected and the wrench of leaving home, while the family is spared the pangs of compelling her to do so. Or, at the other age extreme, consider the mentally ill child so difficult to deal with that his mother is a wreck at the end of the day. If he is home only at night, she can give him the loving care and sense of "this is home" that all children need. As for night and weekend hospitals, when a mentally ill member continues to earn money, the family's financial load is considerably lessened.

In any case, whatever your feelings, do not hesitate to reveal them frankly to the doctor, or to the social workers who are practically always connected with clinics and hospitals and occasionally with doctors in private practice. A social worker is someone especially trained to understand the family situation, to be a good listener, and to counsel with relatives about their own emotions. Moreover, he is familiar with community resources and can help you solve such practical problems as where to get funds if the family wage earner is not producing, how to get care for the children when the mother is absent, or how to locate a good nursing home for an old person who no longer needs psychiatric care but is too infirm to be cared for at home. In some rural regions, public health nurses are the principal resource. Any family with a member who suffers from a mental illness suffers too, but you may find it heartening to discover how many professional helpers and ways the community affords to lessen your troubles. Similarly, there are many ways for helping your relative out of his.

CHAPTER 4

Some Treatments for
Mental Illness

THERE IS NO PANACEA for mental illness. Mental disease, like physical disease, has many forms, with causes as varied as symptoms. So even in magnificently set-up hospitals or outpatient clinics not all the following treatments will be used on any one patient. Consider them simply as some of the ammunition modern science has available in the battle for mental health, and depend upon the doctor's training and experience for determining when and where and how each, alone or in combination, can be effectively used.

One category of treatments for mental illness includes those used to change the way the body functions. Among the treatments that approach mental disorders through altering processes of the nervous system, muscles, glands, or organs are:

DRUG THERAPY

Sometimes called chemotherapy. "Therapy" is the Greek word for treatment. A number of drugs are used to treat mental illnesses. Although the drugs are not in themselves a cure, they do reduce symptoms. Large numbers of tense, overactive, hostile, or noisy patients who have been given these medications have

33

quieted down, have stopped being tormented by their delusions, have behaved more normally, and have become approachable and cooperative. The drugs producing such effects have a variety of trade names, but are generally known as tranquilizers.

Another group of drugs are energizers. These help to raise the spirits of the depressed and to stimulate the withdrawn or apathetic.

Many patients would not be able to stay in the community were it not for drug therapy. Other hospitalized patients could not come home without continuing medication. If one or more of the drugs has been prescribed for your relative—for they are frequently used in combination—make sure that he takes them.

But for all its demonstrated usefulness, drug therapy does not eliminate the necessity for any or all other kinds of treatment. For one thing, it is not suitable for all patients. For another, it does not bring about the self-understanding that might remove the need for chemical props. Its enormous contribution to mental health is that it speeds recovery. Nursing staffs can use their energies to further improvement instead of having to "protect" or "manage." Patients themselves can use their energies for trying to get well instead of dissipating them in abnormal activity or retreat from life.

ELECTROTHERAPY

Also called electroshock or electroconvulsive therapy. A carefully controlled electric current is passed through the brain to produce a fleeting convulsion. Its object is to take the patient sharply out of his world of unreality and render him amenable to taking in and accepting actualities. Shock treatment is painless, unconsciousness is immediate, and the patient has no memory of the treatment. Nevertheless, it is usually preceded by intravenous anesthesia and medication, which bring about relaxation and greatly reduced movements.

After a series of treatments the patient may be confused and have trouble remembering what happened recently, but this condition is tempor: ry and soon disappears. In some cases electrotherapy is completely effective by itself; in some, it opens the way for other therapies. Drug therapy has reduced the use of electrotherapy; but with good results, long and often established, some psychiatrists consider it the preferred treatment for certain conditions, notably depression.

When electroshock is given in full-time hospitals, the patient is of course cared for by the hospital staff, not only during but also before and after the treatment. When it is given in a doctor's office or outpatient clinic, someone in the family, or someone delegated by it, should escort the patient to and from the treatment and give him close supervision and companionship for however many weeks afterward the doctor specifies. The number and frequency of needed treatments vary.

INSULIN COMA TREATMENT

This chemical form of shock therapy, which produces profound unconsciousness, is given in a substantial number of hospitals. Its principal use is in the treatment of schizophrenia, especially when this mental disease is chronic or has not responded well to some other forms of treatment.

ANTIBIOTIC THERAPY

For diseases of the central nervous system, notably general paresis, penicillin is given. By destroying the spirochetes—the organisms causing syphilis—it arrests organic damage to the brain and restores many patients to the community or to usefulness under protective conditions. The earlier in the illness penicillin is given, the better the results.

SURGERY

When abnormal behavior is the result of a brain tumor, surgical removal of the tumor is a well-established procedure.

Another category of treatments includes a broad range of methods of psychotherapy, all having self-understanding as their goal. The physiological treatments that include pills, shock, or antibiotics may precede or accompany psychotherapy, since it requires cooperation, or it may be used exclusively.

Psychotherapy aims to lead a patient to realize why he feels and acts the way he does, and so not only to rid himself of his symptoms, but also to prevent their return. Some forms of psychotherapy are:

INDIVIDUAL PSYCHOTHERAPY

This is a special form of talking things over with a trained professional worker. He may be a psychiatrist or a clinical psychologist or a psychiatric social worker. Although, unlike psychiatrists, such psychologists and social workers have no medical degrees and cannot prescribe drugs, they are schooled and experienced in what makes people think and behave as they do.

PSYCHOANALYSIS

This particular, specialized form of psychotherapy is given by a physician who has had intensive training in psychoanalytic techniques. The patient, talking about whatever comes to mind, brings up stored-away memories of long-forgotten disturbing incidents and re-experiences the emotions aroused when they occurred. Usually psychoanalysis is less effective with the severely than with the mildly ill. Long and arduous, it may take years of almost daily sessions.

PSYCHOANALYTICALLY ORIENTED PSYCHOTHERAPY

Psychoanalytically trained therapists use the principles they have learned for a modified and shorter kind of psychotherapy. It is so widely used and brings such good results that the couch, on which the patient lies with the doctor behind him in orthodox psychoanalysis, is increasingly being replaced by the chair, in which the patient sits facing the doctor, as he would any other.

PLAY THERAPY

Children too young or disturbed to be reached primarily through words are given the run of a playroom containing many carefully chosen toys. When they are wantonly destructive, or throw a papa or mama doll out of a doll house, not only is the psychiatrist able to learn what is troubling them, but they also are discharging their feelings of hostility. Or a too-quiet child who shies away from people may begin to come out of his shell through skillfully induced contact with playthings that he feels will not hurt him. Usually the younger the child, the briefer the necessary period of treatment.

GROUP PSYCHOTHERAPY

In this form of psychotherapy a whole group of patients thrash out their problems together, under the leadership of a skilled psychotherapist. Where a hospital or clinic is understaffed, obviously the method has great practical value, for it enables many patients to benefit by psychotherapy although there would not be enough doctor-hours for each to get it individually. But even in the best-staffed hospitals and clinics and in the offices of private-practice psychiatrists, where each patient could be given all the time needed, it is often either the preferred method or combined with individual psychotherapy. The very participation in meetings with others who express anxieties, hostilities, or fears similar to one's own is a fortifying experience; no one likes to feel uniquely "different." To a person who feels peculiarly weak or unworthy, the support and approval of a group can become more strengthening than that of any individual, even a well-liked and understanding therapist. Likewise the disapproval and criticism of one's peers can be more acceptable and can carry more weight than those of someone, like a doctor, who is in authority. Often in flashes of insight patients gain understanding of their warped emotions and thinking more quickly through group psychotherapy than is possible in individual psychotherapy. Even those who seem to sit quite aloof and do not contribute to the discussion tend to benefit by what is going on. Excellent results have been reported, indeed, with the kind of patients who are seemingly unresponsive and unchangeable, such as the very old.

There are several variations of group psychotherapy, for example:

FAMILY THERAPY   A relatively new kind of group psychotherapy, dating from the 1950's, this takes many forms, but has been so successful that its use is rapidly growing in clinics, in hospitals, and in the private practice of psychiatry. It is based on the idea that each member of the family unit profoundly affects all and all profoundly affect each. Family therapy may consist of joint sessions of patient and spouse, or of patient and parent or parents, or of the whole family group. The therapist, instead of working exclusively with the one who is sick or sickest, gives everyone the opportunity to air his viewpoints and feelings and, as in the usual kind of group psychotherapy, to develop new insights and to change attitudes toward the rest.

PSYCHODRAMA   A form of group psychotherapy, this is sometimes called role-playing. Patients not only talk out their feelings but also act them out. Real-life situations are suggested by the therapist or by the patients themselves, and then the patients— sometimes playing the parts of themselves, sometimes of someone else—dramatize these. Such play-acting expression of their own emotions and reactions to others, the response of other actors in the psychodrama—sometimes hospital or clinic staff members— to what they say and do, and the skillfully interjected comments by the therapist all work toward emotional release and increased self-understanding.

ACTIVITY THERAPY   Suitable for certain children and in certain combinations, in this form of group therapy the youngsters think they are members of a club. They are allowed to use as they wish such things as tools and modeling clay. The therapist is as unobtrusive as possible, allowing the influence of the group to render the behavior of the obstreperous more orderly and to socialize those who keep too much to themselves.

Most of the physiological therapies and all the psychotherapies may be used with either outpatients or hospital patients. Other categories of treatments for mental illness can be developed only in a hospital setting. Some (described in Chapters 10 and 11) may be found in community hospitals, but more typically are a feature of residential mental hospitals. The doctor may tell you that your patient should go to one of these.

CHAPTER 5

Why a Mental Hospital?

THERE ARE A NUMBER of reasons why your relative may not be able to begin treatment in the community or to remain there. Its general hospital may not accept psychiatric patients. It may lack other mental health facilities. Perhaps the facilities it has are not free, and your relative has no money. Perhaps he does not improve under the treatment he is getting. He may injure or neglect himself, or have poor judgment, so that round-the-clock care and protection are needed. A devoted family may have exhausted itself trying to care for him. His unwarranted suspicions, fights, and assaults may endanger the community. But whatever the basis of the doctor's decision, unless you are very different from the relatives of most mental patients, you will have many reasons for thinking that this step of residential hospitalization is too drastic or undesirable.

High on the list may be the conviction, shared by many of those who know nothing about mental hospitals, that it can only make people worse to be around others like themselves. The experience of hospitals in this country since 1773 has shown—difficult though this is for most of us to believe—that the association of mentally ill persons with one another has few adverse effects and some favorable ones.

Do not go upon the premise that for your mentally ill relative to live among other mentally ill men or women is the same as if *you* lived among them. He is sick and they are sick, and he may be better off in their company than in that of the mentally healthy, for they will not overtax his emotional strength. Others will have the same poor memory that he has, or the same difficulties in meeting life, or the same feelings of unworthiness, or fears of incurable illness, or what not. In the hospital he need not compete with the mental vigor of the normal, and this in itself can be soothing.

Soothing, too, can be the tolerance of mental patients for one another's peculiarities. To a degree almost unattainable for normal people, except those professionally concerned with mental illness, the mentally ill disregard one another's annoying habits, bear with being scolded, and discount delusions. Such an atmosphere can be more conducive to tranquility than the criticisms or distress that a mentally sick person is likely to encounter in a world of the mentally well.

Do not refuse to hospitalize—on medical advice—because you are reluctant to put a "stigma" upon your relative. You put a greater stigma upon him by letting him go about making a spectacle of himself. Often, with the greatest embarrassment, recovered mental patients recall their words and actions when they were ill. Surely it is better that silly claptrap or obscenities or outbursts against the people whom normally a patient loves the most be poured out before doctors and nurses than before the neighbors. Mental hospital staffs are at hand for the purpose of dealing with such behavior; they take it unemotionally and hold inviolate revelations not always flattering to the family.

If "what to tell people" is troubling you, solve your problem in the simplest manner, by saying frankly that you are sending your relative to a hospital where he can get care and treatment.

A barefaced lie, you can be sure, will be found out, and any elaborate system of concealment as to his whereabouts will not only put a continual burden on you, but will also make it harder for him to meet his former friends when he is back home again.

It may be the mother or father of young children or of teen-agers who needs hospital care. Generally it is better to have children know that a parent is sick and needs treatment away from home for a while than it is to be "hush-hush" and mysterious about the situation. Of course, just what you are going to say, how you are going to say it, and how much explaining you should do depend largely on the child's age. An excellent booklet, *When a Parent is Mentally Ill: What to Say to Your Child,* by Helene S. Arnstein, contains specific, detailed advice on how best to help children of different ages through the experience of separation and the perhaps even more difficult time before, when a parent had behaved peculiarly. This booklet costs 65 cents and is available from the Child Study Association of America, 9 East 89th Street, New York, New York 10028.

Don't think of the doctor's recommendation in terms of a place where people are "put away." Remember that a modern mental hospital is a hospital like any other, not primarily a place of detention but a health center to which people come to get skilled treatment with the goal of recovery. About three-fourths of all patients leave residential mental hospitals improved, the vast majority of them within the first few months; in the better-staffed and better-equipped hospitals, improvement rates run higher. Besides, if every mental case were treated early enough—too many get help too late—there is no telling how many more patients might be discharged.

Possibly—it is a bitter pill to swallow—conditions at home may aggravate mental illness. There may be too much love, too much solicitude, too much devotion, for a person's emotional good. There may, indeed, with or without the benefit of family therapy, be a perfect balance in all personal relations, yet simply because each of us is so emotionally involved with his family, some mental patients are better off temporarily removed from the joys and sorrows, the frictions and affections, of normal family life. Similarly, pressures on the job may be more than some can tolerate.

Even in the poorest mental institutions, which offer little or nothing in the way of scientific treatment, numbers of patients recover largely because they are removed and protected from the stresses, strains, and entanglements of life among their own people, bosses, or co-workers, and have a chance for an emotional breathing spell in a less charged atmosphere. For some patients the best chance of lessening emotional tensions, of slowing down abnormally geared-up minds, may be in surroundings created especially for their needs and not among the demands and competition of everyday life.

Don't consider the doctor an alarmist and reject his advice to hospitalize because you see so many signs that your relative is "all right again" or is "snapping out of it." Make due allowance for your inevitable wishful thinking. In addition, what you, in your unfamiliarity with mental illness, consider all right may be all wrong! When a depressed patient, for example, suddenly becomes elated, bubbling over, and gleeful it is more than likely that he is as sick as he was before and has simply undergone a change of mood. Conversely, if an excited patient suddenly calms down into silence, he may be in a stupor, more seriously ill than before and not, as you may think, improving. Just as a general physician or internist is able to tell whether an infection has really been conquered or whether disappearance of symptoms is only temporary, so a psychiatrist has means of gauging whether a mental disorder still exists despite periods of apparent mental health. Mood changes, intervals of normality—which in even the most serious cases of mental illness can occur either briefly, several times a day, or for as long as several days or a week at a time—may be only superficial and have no more significance in indicating the patient's real condition than drops in his temperature during certain hours of the day.

Don't delude yourself that, whatever the doctor says about the patient's needs and condition, he is better off at home, under your personal tender care. The best intentions and all the devotion in the world are often no substitutes for the facilities of hospitals. And that goes for mental as well as for general hospitals. Equipment, trained staff, the routine so difficult to establish in the average household, may all play their part in furthering recovery. If there are organic complications, obviously examinations and twenty-four-hour observations can be better made in any hospital than in the usual home.

Perhaps the most imperative among all the reasons for advising hospitalization, the doctor may say that it is dangerous for your relative to be in any place where he cannot be constantly watched. The physician is not thinking only of physical violence, the injury the patient may do to others: that is the least of it. Violence isn't nearly so prevalent among the mentally ill as some of us fancy. Actually the greatest perils of mental illness lie in what patients are likely to do to themselves, with the danger of suicide the most distressing. With the round-the-clock vigilance of a hospital this danger is greatly diminished.

Another danger of which a doctor is thinking when he advises the safety of a residential hospital is the harm a mentally sick person might do to the rest of his family, with weeping spells, demands, tantrums, or extravagance. If he cannot get community treatment, or does not improve under it, he might take up so much of his relatives' time and energy that their emotional endurance and earning capacities suffer. Young children might become emotionally upset.

The fact remains that even if you are willing to sacrifice yourself and other members of your family, your patient himself is better off in a residential hospital if the doctor so advises—whether it be primarily for protection, for active treatment, or for both. And heed the doctor's recommendations, too, as to choice of hospitals, if you are in a position to have any.

CHAPTER 6

Private and Governmental Hospitals

PRIVATE PSYCHIATRIC HOSPITALS are run by nonprofit organizations like foundations or churches, and by individuals—most often psychiatrists—or groups for profit. Rates in some private hospitals, whether nonprofit or not, are high in relation to most people's incomes, although not in relation to what the hospitals give. Most rates of private hospitals, however, compare very favorably with general-hospital rates for surgical, obstetric, psychiatric, or any other kind of patient.

Government hospitals, which are tax-supported, include state, county, and federal. Despite the rapidly increasing, hopeful, and successful psychiatric services in community general hospitals, the bulk of patients who have the major mental illnesses and cause the community the most distress still go to state hospitals.

Of course if you can easily afford the cost of a good private hospital, either because you or your relative has the means, or thanks to health insurance coverage, you will doubtless want to send him there. It will be easier for him to find friends with common interests and tastes, such as golf, reading and bridge, than it would be among the population of a state hospital, where most are poor, many middle-class, and few if any well-to-do. He, and especially she, may be spared humiliating, injurious violations of lifelong habits of privacy, such as having to dress, bathe, and go to the toilet in full view.

Above all, because the ratio of professional staff to patients is so much higher in private hospitals than in governmental hospitals, patients can get more individual attention and more intensive therapy, and so tend to leave faster.

Indeed, even if it is not easy to pay for private hospitalization, its pros and cons ought to be carefully considered. Especially if the patient is a wage earner who will not be earning while he is hospitalized, or who might lose his job if he is away from it a long time, immediate investment in private hospitalization might pay off in the long run.

An important basis for decision is the doctor's opinion as to how long hospitalization may be necessary. Although all he will do is estimate—for no reputable physician makes promises or prophecies—it can make a big difference in your financial planning whether he thinks it will be a matter of weeks or months or years. Most patients' stay in private psychiatric hospitals is about sixty days.

On the other hand, you ought to take into account the needs of other members of the family, and what the effects might be if they are substantially deprived because of the money spent on the patient. Most have probably been annoyed with him anyway, and such frustrations as not being able to take a vacation or having to defer college for a year can grow into resentment, which will not be good for the patient when he comes home.

A social worker is the best person with whom to thrash out your practical perplexities and help you arrive at a sound decision. Some Family Service agencies have workers especially expert in the emotional and family aspects of budgeting; all social workers have had training in family relations. The social worker who is connected with a private hospital you are considering can also be helpful. Many private psychiatric hospitals discourage admission of patients whose families would be under serious financial strain by having them there. This is because family tension can react so badly on the patient that it might impede the hospital's work with him.

Nearly all states license and inspect private hospitals, and where you have the protection of such authority, of course you ought not even consider a mental hospital that is not "licensed" or "approved" or "inspected." Licensure, however, does not necessarily ensure good medical care. Many states set no requirements for the number or qualifications of personnel, but inspect and license only on the basis of such elementary matters as sanitation and fire protection. States with the better public hospitals as a rule have the better private hospitals, although there are outstanding exceptions.

An index of a hospital's reputability is its membership in the National Association of Private Psychiatric Hospitals, 353 Broad Avenue, Leonia, New Jersey 07605. Members must meet certain standards of care and treatment. But if a hospital is not on the membership list, this does not mean that it falls below the association's standards. Some good private psychiatric hospitals have chosen not to join.

The best criterion of quality is accreditation by the Joint Commission on Accreditation of Hospitals. All hospitals will tell you whether they are accredited or not, and usually you will see the certificate of approval in the main lobby, probably along with the license where licensure is required. If the physician does not already know about accreditation and the regulations, ask him to check on them. He is in the best position to recommend the private hospital he considers most suitable for your patient. If there is none he is familiar with personally, ask him to interpret for you the details of the listings in the Directory of the National Association of Private Psychiatric Hospitals.

Unless your relative has to be taken to the hospital in an

emergency, visit it before he enters as a patient. If he is apprehensive but cooperative, there is no reason why he should not go along with you for a preview. Make your financial arrangements in advance, keeping in mind that one hospital that seems to have a lower rate than another may really cost more if there are many charges for extras. An apparently more costly hospital may have charges that are all, or nearly all, inclusive.

Some private hospitals are luxurious and picturesque, while others as good are relatively plain and simple. Do not think that the hospital is just trying to "show off" if its common living quarters are much more inviting and attractive than its bedrooms. This is done deliberately as an inducement for patients who want to mope or dream not to stay by themselves. In any case, unless a hospital is definitely dirty and dilapidated, do not judge it by its buildings. More important than bricks and mortar are staff and program.

In the last analysis, the important things in selecting a private mental hospital are your physician's recommendation and your own impressions after visiting the premises and talking with members of the staff. The best hospital is the one that best meets the needs in your particular instance. This is not necessarily the most expensive; treatment may be better in one hospital than in another that charges more.

As a rule, the Veterans Administration hospitals have more to spend per patient per day than other governmental hospitals, and therefore tend to be better staffed and equipped than most state or county hospitals. If your relative is a veteran, find out from the nearest VA hospital or VA regional office whether he is eligible for VA hospitalization. You will find the VA personnel interested and sympathetic about doing anything for your veteran relative that can come under the law, just as Social Security personnel are about an aged relative. Incidentally, do not overlook the fact that Social Security gives assistance to the needy aged in mental institutions.

Too many state hospitals, regrettably, are behind the times, with more emphasis on protecting patients than on giving them responsibility. But by no means get the impression that your relative cannot get excellent treatment in a state hospital. The good state hospitals are better than inferior private hospitals, and the best of them are in the forefront of modern attacks on mental illness. Some indeed are the core of community treatment. With professional teams of doctors and nurses who travel in the area served by the hospital and stay with the patient before, during, and after hospitalization, they afford the middle class and the poor the same continuity of treatment otherwise possible only with a private psychiatrist. The same, or other state hospitals, feature outpatient clinics or part-time hospital care. But even those state hospitals that do not reach long arms into the community tend to have dedicated, hard-working professional staffs.

Do not let false pride keep you from utilizing the facilities of a state hospital; as a citizen you are entitled to them. Moreover, every state hospital requires maintenance payments equivalent to the actual cost of the patient's care and treatment. If you are unable to pay this, full or partial adjustment will be made.

In most private and a few public hospitals, the psychiatrist who began treating the patient in the community may continue to attend him. Everywhere, however, the psychiatrist's collaboration and cooperation are welcomed by the hospital physician.

Because the known is always less terrifying than the unknown, it is a good idea to pay a visit to the hospital at some time before you bring in your patient. Families placing their relatives in private hospitals usually do this as a matter of course, so that they can inspect it to their satisfaction before reserving a bed. Your state hospital would no more deny you the similar privilege of inspection than your state legislature would forbid you to attend its sessions. Many state hospitals, indeed, are regularly visited by local boards of laymen.

Now, everything in your state hospital will not please you. In any public hospital you are sure to see some things you do not like—perhaps beds crowded close together, perhaps bleak living quarters, perhaps patients kept indoors on pleasant days. In some hospitals you may disapprove of many things, from lack of cleanliness to boredom on the wards, from dreary food to lavatories lacking privacy.

You are also all too likely to be depressed by seeing "old inhabitants." But realize that they either are hangovers from the days when treatment for mental illness was not as effective as it is now, or have no suitable home or family to which they can return.

Unfortunately, state hospitals have always been hampered by shortsighted, penny-pinching legislators. When times are bad their budgets are slashed. When times are good the salaries they are able to offer are not raised enough to compete with what is being offered elsewhere, so they tend to suffer from personnel shortages. In recent years the buildings and equipment of most state hospitals have greatly improved; but most are still understaffed. Although nearly everywhere there have been impressive increases in appropriations, these have failed to keep pace with the cost of living.

Consequently, because of overcrowding and a serious shortage of doctors, nurses, attendants—sometimes even medication—everything needed to help mental patients recover may not be offered, nor may everything that is known be consistently applied. But so fantastic is many people's image of what an "asylum" for the mentally ill is like, that the reality, at worst, is likely to be better than what you imagined.

You will see, wandering about the grounds or peacefully at work, numbers of men and women "who don't look at all crazy" and whom you often cannot distinguish from employees. In any modern hospital the great majority of windows have no bars; there are no locked gates; and most, perhaps all, wards and buildings are likewise unlocked. Nearly all mental hospitals have beautiful, well-cared-for grounds. The general atmosphere is quiet and easygoing; there is actually less bustle and noise in the corridors than in a general hospital.

Though, as a rule, in states having more than one state hospital mental patients are allocated according to district, it is often possible to arrange for admission to the state hospital that, for one reason or another, you or the patient prefers. No more than private hospitals are public hospitals places to which people are sent as punishment. They exist to give service to those who need their protection, care, and treatment.

Well over half the states have joined with one another in an arrangement called Compact. This provides that if a patient is not a legal resident of a state in which he has had to be hospitalized, he may either remain where he is or be transferred to another Compact state. Usually the reason for transfer is that the patient's family lives there. A request for transfer may be initiated by the patient, the family, or the hospital, but the patient's welfare determines whether or not it is granted. If there is a transfer, transportation is provided from public funds, as a rule those of the state from which the patient is sent.

Compact is just one of the newer, heartening recognitions of the rights of mental patients and of the importance of family and community in their treatment. Changes for the better in laws of admission to governmental hospitals are another.

CHAPTER 7

Getting the Patient Admitted

HAVING ACCEPTED the mental illness for what it is, having decided to hospitalize and selected the hospital, you must now arrange for admission. In the growing number of states that have brought their mental health laws up-to-date, the procedure is likely to be simple and painless. In the minority that have not, it can be distasteful. But obviously you must obey the law in order for your troubled relative to secure the haven and help he needs, so about all you can do is grit your teeth and go through with the legal red tape as promptly and unemotionally as you can.

If you show distress before your relative, break down and cry in his presence, or express to him any objections to his being hospitalized at this or at any other time during his illness, you will only add to his confusion and distress, or may strengthen his feelings of persecution, if he suffers from them.

About 90 per cent of the mentally ill are not dangerous to themselves or others, and provided they were properly prepared, good medical care was available, and laws permitted, could be admitted safely to hospitals on medical decision alone. "Insanity" laws of the past, however, were not based on the assumption that speedy help should be available to the sick. Instead, they aimed to make admission difficult, because of the unwarranted fear that "sane" people might be "railroaded" into hospitals by unscrupulous relatives or enemies to get them out of the way. Where such laws stand largely unchanged, it may be because of state legislators' ignorance or indifference; or it may be because of the influence of powerful, well-financed groups who write and speak of "plots" by the government, psychiatrists, and the mental health movement.

Actually, detention in a mental hospital of someone who should never have gone there is extremely rare, virtually nonexistent. To be sure, among the patients there may be some unfortunate epileptics whose minds are normal, for epilepsy does not necessarily bring about mental illness. But in the minority of cases in which seizures cannot be successfully controlled by medication and are too frequent and severe for patients to be cared for at home, there is often no other place for them to go for long-term care and treatment.

Similarly, some unmanageable "behavior-problem" children, although not mentally ill, occupy beds for want of a more suitable place in the community.

Mental hospitals are also likely to have in their population a sprinkling of the mentally retarded who are not mentally ill. Mental illness differs from mental retardation. Mental illness is a condition in which something goes wrong with the mind, like a wall that becomes warped; mental retardation is a condition in which the mind has never fully developed, like a wall that has not been completed. The special institutions for the mentally retarded are usually called schools. Nearly all state schools have such long waiting lists, however, that when someone is too infantile or childish to get along in the world, the mental hospital may take him in even though no illness has developed in such mind as he has.

All this only demonstrates, however, a woeful lack of proper facilities, not "railroading"! What is more, if a mentally well person without some special disability did land in a mental hospital, you may be sure he would quickly be out of it. Overworked staff, quite aside from any humanitarian motives, are much more eager to release patients than to keep them confined.

Fortunately for your relative and you, today the emphasis on legal protection of the patient against supposed evildoers is rapidly giving way to emphasis on medical protection of his mental health. Modern mental health laws do not lump everybody, but allow for the differences and degrees in mental illness. Judicial formalities that used to delay admission on even a temporary or emergency basis, no matter how much the patient's condition worsened or his family was upset, have almost disappeared. Changes in wording of statutes and of documents, which patient or family had to sign in most states, make hospitalization much less of an ordeal for both. Shame and guilt can be stirred up by terms that smack of criminality, like "commitment," or of superstition, like "lunacy"—a hangover from the days when the moon (*luna*) was thought to govern the behavior of the mentally ill—as they are not by those according with present knowledge: "hospitalization" or "mental illness." The great majority of states no longer use the word "insanity," a purely legal word without medical meaning. Just how your relative is to be admitted will depend, of course, on both his condition and where you live. The local mental health association or his doctor can advise you.

A number of states provide for "informal admission" on exactly the same basis as patients are admitted to a general hospital. There is no written application, no agreement to stay in the hospital for a specified period of time.

All the states but Alabama provide for "voluntary admission." This requires merely the patient's signing the necessary paper in the office of the hospital's admitting physician, or, if he is under sixteen or eighteen, depending on the state, a parent's or guardian's signature. The form of the paper varies with the particular hospital and the particular state. When all it involves is a statement that the signer understands the nature of the hospital, promises to obey its rules, and will give a specified three to ten days' notice before leaving, it is less painful than in the few remaining places where he must declare himself insane.

Informal and voluntary admissions are the best means of opening the doors of a mental hospital, because, by everyone's experience, they are the usual way people go to hospitals. When someone needs an operation on his foot, for example, he is not ordinarily taken willy-nilly to the surgical ward of a general hospital, but is consulted beforehand and goes of his own free will. As a rule, therefore, physically ill men and women enter hospitals recommended by their orthopedists or other physicians, ready to cooperate with the institution and its staff. Mental patients who need no admission papers or sign their own can have similar readiness for treatment in hospitals recommended by their psychiatrists.

It may be surprising that many persons realize they have a serious mental illness and welcome medical assistance. Indeed, it is not unheard of for an individual unattended by friend or relative, to walk into a mental hospital and say, "Something's gone wrong with me; will you help me here?" Certain types of mental disorders, for instance, carry with them a fear of losing self-control. Depressed patients often recognize the abnormality of their abysmally low spirits. Some with delusions of persecution, complaining that their enemies give them no rest, deprive them of sleep, and ruin their digestion, say they will be only too glad to have the benefits of shelter and care. Even the excited, who believe themselves completely rational, may admit they are "overwrought" and "nervous" and need treatment. A few patients, too, agree to voluntary admission as a lesser evil than court commitment. But do not use threats to bring about voluntary admission. Let the doctor do the talking.

A substantial number, although unwilling or unable to bring themselves to make voluntary application, may accept hospitalization when their doctors and families tell them it is necessary. Nearly one-third of the states provide for "nonprotesting admission." It may be had simply by the certification of one or more physicians on condition that the patient does not at least object, and is especially useful and acceptable for the elderly and infirm who suffer from one of the more severe mental disorders of old age.

Sometimes, of course, such desirable forms of admission as informal, voluntary, or nonprotesting are practically, although not legally, impossible. Just as some general hospital patients, very ill or unconscious, must be admitted on the say-so of someone more responsible, so mental patients not sufficiently reasonable to cooperate must have decisions made for them. They are the 10 per cent estimated by psychiatrists to need compulsory admission. Your relative is most likely to be among them if he is old and very confused. But he might also be younger and confused, or quite disturbed.

Similarly, a decision as to whether it is all right to leave the hospital may have to be made for a patient, even though he entered it voluntarily, informally, or nonprotestingly. He may have grown worse or more irresponsible, for there can be setbacks and relapses in mental illnesses as in others. He may be doing fine in the protective hospital, but in the hospital's opinion needs to stay a while longer because on his own the chances are he would be dangerous to himself and others. When such patients cannot be persuaded to stay on their own volition, there is the resource of compulsory detention by a court, for a time period varying with the state.

In some states nonjudicial compulsory admissions are the only kind. Somewhat over half the states provide for them. The entering wedge may be a hearing or an investigation or both by a board or commission, or it may be medical certification.

Well over half the states provide for or require court orders in cases of involuntary hospitalization. A member of the family or a friend or an officer of the health or police department has to start things off with a sworn statement, accompanied by the certificates of two physicians. Usually the physicians are appointed by the court, although in some states the family physician may be one of the examiners. If he brings along a colleague whom the patient knows he is in the habit of consulting, the whole procedure can be quite natural. Except where your mental invalid is at such a pitch of emotion that he objects to any kind of examination by anyone, the doctors' part in the proceedings is ordinarily not distressing. Often they will come to your home. If the patient resents their presence, let them do the explaining. After all, doctors are accustomed to dealing with strangers, and you may be sure they will try to make the examination as easy as possible for all concerned.

What they will probably do is first talk with the patient's relatives over the phone. They will introduce themselves to the patient—"I'm Dr. So-and-So"—and in talking with him they will study his mood, the way he talks, the reasonableness of his ideas, and his memory. In some instances they may make a brief physical examination.

And so far as the patient is personally subjected to any procedure, that may be all. In some states the physicians' certificates are enough for admission to a mental hospital and residence for ten to thirty days. During that period there is time for a copy to go to the judge, who can then sign an order providing for residence as long as the hospital authorities think the patient will benefit by it. There is also time for the patient to have improved sufficiently to decide on voluntary or informal admission in such states as provide for these.

Unhappily, however, there are still some states where the patient must undergo court proceedings. Either he must appear before a judge, or, less harassing, the court, in the person of a judge or clerk, comes to him. Fortunately, most judges do not set themselves up as psychiatrists but are guided by the medical opinion. Also fortunately, most are humane, cause no unnecessary discomfiture for patient or family, and often conduct only perfunctory hearings.

No states make jury trial mandatory. In a few, it is held on demand of the patient or someone on his behalf. For mental patients to undergo the ordeal of trial by jury, however, is about as sensible as calling in the neighbors to diagnose appendicitis or polio. Rarely is a jury trial requested.

In some states admission to private psychiatric hospitals is easier than to state hospitals; in no state, harder.

A judicial order of commitment to a mental hospital in some states deprives the patient not only of his liberty but also of the rights to control his property until he is again declared sane by a court. Where there are more modern provisions—as, for instance, in New York, Illinois, and the District of Columbia— patients' civil rights are as carefully guarded as their medical rights to treatment are facilitated. They may communicate by sealed mail with the court that ordered their hospitalization, as well as with others; they may receive visitors, and they may vote unless they have been specifically declared incompetent. They have the right to dispose of property and to make contracts and purchases, such as subscribing to magazines or acquiring television sets and radios while they are in the hospital. Also, they may bring criminal charges against their wrongful detention or denial of rights.

By and large, courts have ruled that hospitalization as such does not affect the validity of a will. Though many forgetful or resentful patients in mental hospitals are not capable of making wills that would stand up under controversy, many other patients are.

In certain states there is automatic court appointment of a guardian of a patient's property. In most of the larger states appointment of such a guardian is made by application to a court and is done only when the patient has sufficient funds to justify the expense of the proceedings.

As long ago as 1827 New York State passed a statute forbidding the care of mental patients in jails or houses of correction, and many other states have followed suit. Although some do not seem to have caught up with such enlightenment, even in those states that prohibit jailing of the sick the law may be flouted. Probably the main reason is lack of other places where the mentally ill can stay pending admission to a mental hospital. Other reasons are many general hospitals' refusal to admit them, public ignorance and indifference to their plight, and occasionally the tendency of well-meaning policemen to put anyone whose behavior seems odd into traditional local confinement. Detention in jail of someone who is sick is outrageous from the point of view of humanity, science, and common sense, so if there is any way in which you can possibly keep your relative at home until he can get into the hospital, do so.

CHAPTER 8

Taking the Patient to the Hospital

BECAUSE A FAVORABLE ATTITUDE toward the hospital gives a patient a head start on his journey to mental health, there are desirable and undesirable methods of taking him there.

Least desirable is transportation from jail or home in the company of a sheriff or some other officer of the law. This tends to make a mentally disordered person feel as if he were a criminal about to be punished—which he is not—rather than a deeply troubled person about to be helped—which he is. Wherever it is possible to avoid having a law-enforcement officer as escort, do not enlist one. So very few of the mentally ill are violent that this kind of assistance is hardly ever a real necessity.

The most up-to-date mental health laws specify that whenever possible a relative should be allowed to accompany the patient on the trip to the hospital. In most states a woman patient must be accompanied by a woman appointed by the court, unless her husband, father, son, or brother goes along.

In certain states it is required by law that an attendant or nurse from the hospital must call for the patient, upon request or notification of the state hospital, and accompany him to his destination. Where it is not required by law your request may or may not be granted, but at any rate it is worth the try if your patient is reluctant to go to the hospital. Many an exhausted and distraught family has been amazed to see a patient, thoroughly unmanageable by those near and dear to him, turn cooperative at the first quiet words of a hospital employee and go willingly with him or her. The poise and assurance that come with training and experience can act like balm upon obstreperous patients or evoke a response from those who isolate themselves.

Make it quite clear, however, that the escort has come with your consent, and be present when your relative leaves home. The object of this is to give him no grounds for thinking that he has been snatched from the bosom of his family by a kidnapper. It is better to endure his storming at you than to have him hostile toward the hospital that offers his best hope for recovery. Once he is well, he will no longer resent your giving him the opportunity for treatment but, on the contrary, will be grateful for it.

If the patient is physically as well as mentally ill, send for an ambulance. Ambulance service may be available from hospitals or the police or fire departments, or from a private firm. You may wish to check the cost, if any, before ordering an ambulance.

In preparing your patient for the trip there is one rule for all relatives of mental patients. Be the patient willing or unwilling to go to a mental hospital, be he transported with professional assistance or without it, do not lie to him. Even force is preferable to deception. Let him find himself in the admission office of a mental hospital when you have said you were taking him on a trip or for a visit, and he will have so little confidence in you and in the hospital, into which he has been tricked, that prospects of voluntary admission are slim indeed. Furthermore, he will begin his hospital stay not with the attitude of cooperation and trust, which wins half the battle for mental health, but with resentment and suspicion, which handicap him at the start. Because mental invalids are unsure of themselves, whether their illness takes the form of braggadocio or self-abasement, they are more sensitive than healthy people to being let down by others.

Do not assume that because your patient is confused, antagonistic, or does not seem to be hearing a word you say, you might as well just bundle him up and carry him off without bothering with any explanation. Many recovered mental patients have expressed great gratitude for the frankness shown them when they were most seriously ill and apparently oblivious to everything that was going on.

On the other hand, do not expect to have the reasonable conversational give and take that you had with your relative before he fell ill. Never argue with a mental patient. Not only are quarrels as injurious to people who are mentally ill as to people who have heart trouble, but also they will get you nowhere. Tell your relative firmly and quietly what you have arranged to do, and do it. Be calm and determined; show him you have made up your mind that he is to go where he will have care and treatment, that none of his antics or pleadings will swerve you from your decision. This is easier said than done, but if you can manage to keep yourself under control, you will save both yourself and him much unnecessary and harmful stress and strain.

Unless it is an emergency admission, take your patient on a weekday, in the daytime, when more of the hospital's personnel are on duty and can give you and the patient the best attention. If your first visit to a large hospital is the day you bring him in and there are no printed directions to the admissions office at the entrance, stop and ask the way from anyone you see within the grounds. Request at the admission office that someone help you with your relative if he balks at going inside.

The patient should have with him such ordinary necessities for a stay overnight or so as a change of hosiery and underwear, nightwear, and toilet articles. It is quite all right to include books and magazines and a few favorite possessions such as trinkets and snapshots. However, do not send to the hospital, upon admission, nor give to your relative at any time during his stay, anything you cannot afford to lose because of its sentimental or monetary value, or anything whose inspection by Tom, Dick, or Harry would be embarrassing. Large sums of money, jewelry, legal documents, family papers, and the like, therefore, are out. Articles have a way of disappearing frequently and mysteriously at mental hospitals. Though you may feel sure, rightly or wrongly, that your patient is quite capable of caring for his own possessions, remember that there are other, more irresponsible patients, who, as part of their illness, take what belongs to others. However, pocket money, pocketbooks, wallets, and other personal effects are, of course, acceptable.

Some hospitals do not permit any patients to have in their possession sharp-pointed instruments like pocketknives, scissors, or nail files. Most, however, confiscate such objects only if a patient is intensely suicidal.

The details of admission procedure vary somewhat in different hospitals, but as a rule you will be received by someone to whom you will hand over the commitment papers, if any. He or she will then get the physician who is the admitting officer, or will take you to his office.

If your relative goes to a private or public residential hospital after treatment in the community, you have probably already given all the information you can to a private-practice psychiatrist, clinic, or psychiatric service of a general hospital, and the hospital to which he is being admitted will have the records. If not, the admitting physician or a social worker will want to make notes on certain data—your relationship to the patient, from where he was brought, the approximate dates of the first signs of mental disorder, what these signs were, the specific incidents that led to hospitalization, something about the family history, the patient's personal history and his past and present reactions to life's problems, his education, and other points helpful in guiding physicians in their diagnoses and treatment for mental illness. Do not let any feeling of false pride or obligation to your relative prevent you from giving whatever information is requested; be completely frank. Thorough understanding of all important events in the patient's previous life is material in having his illness understood well and treated adequately. The doctor or social worker, you will find, will be receptive and understanding when you pour out your own reactions and worries in regard to your sick relative, and will keep your confidences.

Ask the social worker, or whoever admits the patient, what he will need in the way of clothing. Probably you will be given a list. Relatives are frequently appalled by what seems the extravagant number of changes of washables that a hospital requires —about double, perhaps, what the patient habitually has. The reason is that in an institution it takes about a week for laundry to be returned. If you cannot afford to meet the hospital's wardrobe requirements, say so at once instead of stalling. Your relative will be the sufferer if the hospital keeps on expecting garments to arrive any day instead of making immediate provision to supply him when the family cannot.

Do not insist on going along to the patient's room or ward. You will have ample opportunity to see it later when you visit. Parting is never easy, and prolonging the agonies is likely to cause a scene that will be upsetting to you, to your relative, and to other patients. Make your farewell as casual as you can. Say something like "Good-by, I'll see you soon," and, no matter what names your relative calls you or how vehemently he proclaims that it is you, and not he, who should be left behind, or how plaintively he tells you you are a cruel and ungrateful child, ask him to write often and promise "I'll write, too."

On the other hand do not rush away so that no one at the hospital has time to talk with you further. Certain things should be done before you go. Possibly you might be asked to take back with you some garment like a man's bulky overcoat or a woman's fur coat which the patient has worn on the way to the hospital.

Sometimes when this happens relatives jump to the despairing conclusion that their patient is expected either to die or never to get out. But such a request need give you no reason for gloom; behind it is simply lack of storage space.

You may wish to leave a few dollars to be on deposit for the patient's personal use, for stamps and for little luxuries such as tobacco, candy, or toilet articles.

Finally, find out who will give information on your patient's progress. To be kept dangling on the telephone for half an hour, or shunted from one person to another when calling to inquire about relatives, is disheartening to anxious families. The discouraging impression that a patient is lost in a vast institution, with no one knowing who or where he is and no one looking after him, can be avoided by a simple inquiry on admission. In some hospitals you will be told to ask for the doctor in charge; in others, for the social worker or the physician who is personally taking care of your relative.

And now go about your business with the assurance that in one way or another the hospital has already begun its healing work. Every mental patient does not get well, of course, any more than every patient who goes into a general hospital after a heart attack or for an operation gets out of it alive. But your attitude should rightfully be one of hope. Even from the poorest hospitals, three out of four newly admitted patients leave recovered or improved. In the better hospitals, of course, the chances of leaving are much higher.

A sense of relief and liberation goes along with getting rid of a difficult person. But far from enjoying such legitimate and normal reactions, you may be overwhelmed by guilt at experiencing them. You may be emotionally upset or cry for days on end, even though the thinking part of you knows that hospitalization was wise and right and backed by medical advice. If you are unable to reason yourself out of such feelings, call upon your physician or clergyman or social worker to help you overcome them.

Here again, your attitude and actions are important for both your relative's welfare and your own; even though he is now in the hospital's care, patient and family alike will be beneficiaries of your sensible and informed behavior.

CHAPTER 9

The First Few Days

USUALLY TREATMENT begins with almost immediate participation in hospital activities. It is remarkable how soothing the hospital atmosphere soon is to most patients, and how amiably they comply with the requests of nurses and attendants. For the small minority who remain agitated even at a hospital, doctors soon prescribe effective medication.

If your relative is in a very small private hospital or a private hospital that excludes certain types of mental disorders, he will probably mingle right away with all the other patients. If he is in a governmental hospital, as a rule he will be in its "receiving" or "admissions" or "intensive-treatment" section, called "service" or "ward." Unlike a ward in a general hospital, a mental hospital ward is likely to consist of a group of rooms such as dormitory, dayroom, and dining room.

One reason for keeping the more recently admitted patients together is that they can get the most thorough treatment the hospital affords. The majority of governmental hospitals, unhappily, are so understaffed that if the staff-patient ratio were identical throughout the institution, doctors', nurses', and therapists' time

68

and skills would be spread so thin that nobody at all could benefit. Regretful though the hospital staffs are, therefore, that they
cannot provide the utmost everywhere, they tend to concentrate
on the new patients who have the best chances for recovery, with
the aim to prevent their ever becoming oldtimers.

Do not, however, think that there is something wrong with the
hospital where you have taken your relative if you find it has
no special receiving or admission service. A small but growing
number of state hospitals immediately place new patients in wards
composed of others from their own communities. This is to prevent the upset of being abruptly cut off from community ties.
Often in such hospitals the "team" of doctors and nurses who
treat the patient are no strangers; they had begun treating him
in his home town. In either case, and whatever the theory or
system, your relative may go directly home without ever being
moved to another part of the hospital.

The procedures shortly after admission are about the same in
governmental psychiatric hospitals, private psychiatric hospitals,
and general hospitals. The patient may have a routine body inspection for bruises and other marks, and a nurse will take his
temperature and pulse. Then a doctor will see him for a physical
examination as thorough as one made in any other kind of hospital.

Not only do many mental illnesses have a physical basis, but
a mentally ill person may also be suffering from a physical illness, for instance, arthritis or diabetes. Evidence of overdosage
of drugs, evidence of alcoholism or of infection is sought. Whatever the doctors think necessary—an X ray, a basal metabolism
test, a blood count, an electrocardiogram, a blood test for
syphilis, an electroencephalogram (an electrical record of the
brain currents, analogous to the electrocardiogram's record of
heartbeats) is ordered and made in the hospital's laboratories.

On the basis of the medical checkup the doctor prescribes
medication, surgery, or other treatment, as a doctor would pre-

scribe it in any part of a general hospital. Meanwhile nurses and attendants, at regular intervals, have been taking notes on the patient's behavior—how he talks, acts, eats, sleeps. Also, a social worker may visit his home to get a well-rounded and more detailed understanding of the circumstances under which the patient became ill. A staff doctor will have a "psychiatric interview" with the patient, that is, talk with him to find out his ideas, views, fantasies, or delusions.

Probably there will be a psychological examination too. The psychologist who gives it is a scientist specially trained in testing and evaluating mental processes, emotions, and behavior. The psychological examination may or may not include an intelligence test. Usually its main purpose is to find out not how bright the patient is, but rather what he thinks about, how he reacts to people and things, and how he feels about himself and others. Psychologists have devised many methods by which emotions are revealed. Among these are showing pictures to the patient and asking him to tell the story they suggest. Or he may be shown a series of inkblots and asked to describe what he sees in them, or be asked to draw a person or a house. The psychologist, as skilled in interpreting what emotions, inner conflicts, or distorted thinking show up in such tests as a medical doctor is in interpreting the findings of the laboratory, makes a written report on what he has discovered.

As soon as possible there will be an interview with a vocational rehabilitation counselor, who will ask the patient about his vocational skills and tell him something about how to upgrade or refresh those he has, or how he can acquire some if he is unskilled. If the patient's condition permits, a test of his vocational aptitudes and bents might be given then and there. But the main object of the interview is to start the patient thinking immediately about what he is going to do when he gets out of the hospital, as an incentive to both trying to become well and wanting to improve himself.

Within a few days the doctor, who has talked with the patient frequently and has studied the psychologist's and social worker's reports and the ward notes, sums up his findings. At a staff meeting of department heads the patient may be brought into the conference room, asked if there is anything he would like to say, and studied as he talks. The staff members involved with the case then discuss it and make a considered group decision on further treatment procedures.

The patient is regularly visited by his ward physician. Progress notes or ward notes similar to those first kept continue to be made. If physically well enough, the patient, in most hospitals, is assigned certain light duties to perform for himself and for other patients, although he may not yet be given any regular occupation.

After a week or so the physicians are usually in a position to determine the patient's treatment plan for the immediate future and to make a careful, well-grounded report to his family, to his family physician or the psychiatrist who certified his admission, or to a court if his is one of the cases in which a judge is still waiting to sign some legal papers.

Some patients, especially if they are on effective medication, make enough progress to be released within the first week. Most, however, require further treatment.

CHAPTER 10

Inside a Mental Hospital

MEANWHILE YOU, back home, may be worrying and wondering, "Do they understand him? Will they be good to him?"

The answer to the first question is that if "they" do not understand him at a mental hospital, nobody ever will. All the training and experience of those in charge have been directed toward one end—understanding and helping mental patients.

As for being good to your relative, the personnel of mental hospitals are, on the whole, gentle and kindly people. Every once in a while a lurid story has come out in the newspapers that a mental patient was manhandled. Not only were such abuses always exceptions; they also were more often caused by frightened, untrained attendants having to care for too many disturbed, assaultive patients than by deliberate brutality. Today physical abuse is virtually nonexistent. Thanks to the tranquilizing drugs, the bulk of patients are so manageable that employees are free of fear that they might have to defend themselves.

Moreover, nowadays most hospitals have prescribed training courses for attendants. Some also give more advanced courses for practical nurses and for psychiatric aides, a newer category of persons who work directly with patients on the wards. Psychiatric aides learn about the nature of mental illnesses, the way in which mental patients behave, and the best methods of enhancing their care and treatment.

Many hospitals are affiliated with nursing schools, and patients benefit from the interest and freshness of young student nurses. Graduate nurses—some of whom are known as registered nurses —are frequently in charge of direct day-by-day care of the patients. In the better hospitals these nurses have had additional training in psychiatric nursing.

True, in the handful of states where politics rather than qualifications determine who is employed in state hospitals, nursing personnel may not be as professionally trained as they should be. But even in the poorest mental hospitals you will always find a proportion of attendants who are sincerely devoted to their work and have a natural gift for dealing with mental invalids.

When something goes wrong in a mental hospital—as it is likely to go wrong in any institution or, for that matter, anywhere—it makes excellent copy to play up sensationally and so receives disproportionate public attention. It also gives rise to unwarranted suspicions that many similar instances never come to light. Against the sensational stories that you may have heard or read, weigh these less spectacular facts:

In every mental hospital an employee who uses physical violence against a patient is subject to instant dismissal, unless the use of force is absolutely necessary to save his or her own life. Punishment of patients is nowhere a hospital policy. All hospitals have some system of supervision of attendants.

In addition to visits to the wards by physicians, there are visits by supervisors. These are usually women—though sometimes men—who are mature, experienced, and the most capable among the nurses, psychiatric aides, and attendants. In good hospitals they make regular tours day and night, turn up unexpectedly at odd times, and are at hand immediately where special attention to any patient's need is in order.

If your relative has entered the hospital with apprehension, more than likely after the first strangeness has worn off he is finding many features of his experience there interesting and, indeed, agreeable. He discovers that the ward employees, though very much occupied, are interested in his comfort, and that they work not against but for the patients. He sees flowers and little conveniences that are evidence of someone's plans for his comfort and happiness. In some mental hospitals each new patient receives a personal letter from the superintendent, assuring him that the superintendent is interested in his case and that everything will be done to make his hospital stay pleasant and curative.

Your relative may be visited by a social worker, who helps him to accept the fact that he really needs to be in a hospital, assuages some of his worries by attending to any business he has left unfinished in his community, and acts as a tactful go-between with relatives against whom he harbors resentment because they "put me here." Also, if he (or she) has left dependent children or helpless old people behind at home, the social worker arranges to have them cared for by the proper agencies.

One of these is Homemaker Service. Homemakers are women, usually middle-aged, trained not only to take over the housekeeping but also to understand and adapt to the people they serve. Sent out and supervised sometimes by a public, sometimes a private agency, a homemaker, should she have to be absent, is replaced by another homemaker. Not all Homemaker Services serve all kinds of families or individuals in distress: some, for instance, are restricted to serving recipients of public welfare; some, to those who can pay; some, to old people; some, to families with young children. But the chance of being able to get a homemaker is worth the risk of disappointment upon inquiry. You can check on whether one might be available in your community in your situation, without necessarily the help of a social worker, by consulting the National Directory of Homemaker Services at your local library, or by ordering it (price: $1.50) from the Superintendent of Documents, U.S. Government Printing Office, Washington, D.C. 20402.

Don't be concerned if your relative is moved from the section of the hospital to which he was first assigned or assume that this means he is relegated to lifetime hospitalization. Indeed, the move may signify quite the opposite: that he is now well enough to become a working patient, or that he has improved sufficiently to be housed with patients less ill than the acute cases on the receiving service. Some patients whose prospects for recovery are excellent are moved to disturbed wards because their noisiness or restlessness discommodes other, quieter patients. Or the receiving ward or building may be small in relation to the rest of the hospital, so that patients are moved out of it as soon as possible to make room for new admissions. On the other hand, if the receiving service is relatively large, patients may be kept there until the day of discharge.

In short, whether your relative remains on the admission service for some time or is transferred from it early during his hospitalization is determined by a number of factors varying with different mental hospitals, and is often evidence of administrative practice rather than the patient's condition.

Similarly, any move from one ward to another may be for any of a number of reasons. Transfer within the hospital is not a punishment. Even when it is made because the patient breaks regulations, it is not a disciplinary measure. It is a protective measure. The physician feels that the patient is not yet well enough to adjust to the ward he has been on, and that for a while he may get along better elsewhere.

Also, there is a relatively new kind of classification called the "unit system," in most Veterans Administration hospitals and many state hospitals. This is not based on the patient's age (except for children) or condition, but is done to ensure continuing treatment by the same professional team throughout his stay.

An increasing number of hospitals no longer segregate men and women, but have them share dayrooms, dining rooms, and recreational activities. Experience has shown that few patients are so sick or so old that they do not perk up, take more interest in their appearance, and behave more normally in the presence of the opposite sex.

Many private hospitals have no locked doors. Some public hospitals are also entirely open, as practically all are in Great Britain. In every hospital many wards are kept unlocked all day. Other wards are "semiopen," that is, doors are unlocked at least part of the day and patients may go unattended within a restricted distance outdoors. Some wards are "closed." These are ordinarily kept locked, with physicians and ward personnel carrying the keys. Even in closed wards some patients have ground privileges.

In any good modern mental hospital, your relative will be given all the freedom and responsibility he is able to take. He is likely, for instance, to get his food at a cafeteria instead of having it served to him. Or, even in an expensive private hospital where the heavy work is done by paid employees, he is expected to take care of his own room. The very assumption that a person is responsible usually stimulates him to be less irresponsible.

Patients' improvement with each new assumption of responsibility is the basis of a kind of treatment called "the therapeutic community." This is essentially a democracy in which patients, as well as staff, have their say. They have meetings with doctors, nurses, and therapists in which they plan, make suggestions, and voice complaints and criticisms. They may arrange for parties, publish a newspaper, or form committees for self-government. Medical and nursing personnel do not sit in cold authority in offices off limits to patients, but are readily accessible. In a growing number of hospitals nurses wear good-looking street clothes, not uniforms; in addition to eliminating a symbol of authority, this is a subtle example to women patients inclined to neglect their appearance. There are therapeutic communities, too, in general, day or night hospitals, but their greatest scope is in the residential hospital.

Another form of treatment, though used in community hospitals, likewise has its greatest importance in mental hospitals. Called "milieu therapy" from the French word for environment or surroundings, it embraces everything affecting the patient—from cheerful curtains, pictures on the walls, and comfortable armchairs to the way an attendant speaks to him. One of the objectives of milieu therapy is to render the real world more satisfying than the worlds of fantasy into which the mentally ill have retreated. This, also, is the purpose of treatment through activity.

CHAPTER 11

Activities in a Mental Hospital

ONE OF THE BEST means known for bringing those who have retreated into a world of dreams and fantasies back to reality is work, and every encouragement to useful employment is given. Patients are not driven. Though as an important part of their treatment they are made to feel that they are expected to perform certain duties, they are not threatened either. The need of the patients for something to do is usually greater than the number of necessary tasks to be done.

At private hospitals patients do not do the work necessary to keep the place going, but so great is the health-giving value of work, that such essential activities as cooking, office work, or gardening are occasionally prescribed.

In inferior hospitals the danger of idleness is far greater than the danger of exploitation or overwork.

If a mental patient's condition is such that he doesn't want to work, doesn't want to talk, doesn't want to play, or doesn't want to eat because any reality is an interruption to his imaginings, he can no more be "forced" than someone exhausted by pernicious anemia can be "forced" to hammer stones. Usually, however, he can be induced to work. A dust rag, for instance, put into the hands of someone lost in meditation may be a simple means for helping him take the first step toward normal activity.

Next, with several other patients, he may push a lawn mower; this is an elementary beginning of working with other people. Having acquired the habit of working, he is given chores that, step by step, require more and more of his attention on the job and less on himself and his fantasies.

In many hospitals trained occupational or industrial therapists, in consultation with physicians and with physicians' approval, are in charge of work placement. Social background and education are taken into account in the selection of the person for the job. Job preferences are respected, and if a patient requests a shift from one type of work to another, that preference is respected, too. Mental hospital staffs are under no pressure to place their patients in uncongenial occupations. The inhabitants of governmental hospitals, at any rate, are such a cross section of the population that someone can practically always be found who is willing, accustomed, and usually eager to do every kind of work.

Many hospitals pay for work done by patients. A frequent arrangement is for the hospital to be a subcontractor for some large company. This gives the patients not only a chance to earn but also a healthful feeling of identification with important enterprise. When the paid work is done within the hospital, wages are likely to be less than they would be for the same work outside. If you suspect that your relative is being exploited under this system, discuss your feeling with the physician, social worker, or superintendent, or encourage the patient to do so. But do not jump to indignant conclusions. The difference in pay has the healthful objective of stimulating patients to try to get well so that they can leave the hospital and do better for themselves.

A number of hospitals have counselors from the state Vocational Rehabilitation Agency assigned to them full- or part-time.

Such counselors are not so much concerned with the work a patient does in the hospital as with his career after he leaves. They keep reminding him that his chances for employment will be greatest if he has some skill to offer; they administer aptitude tests and often give practice in employment interviews right in the hospital. Patients may upgrade their skills, learn new ones, or take refresher courses in the ones by which they formerly earned their living. But usually the training is arranged to be given after they are back in the community. The vocational counselor or a counselor from the state Employment Service also keeps patients informed about jobs in the area.

While some patients are at work others, who are mentally sicker, engage in simple activities like rolling balls or tearing strips for hooked rugs. Some exercise in the gymnasium or engage in sports on the athletic field; still others go to the occupational therapy workshop. There, occupational therapists provide them with carefully prescribed, graded, and planned occupations, including finger painting, metalworking, needlework, weaving, and furniture making. They attain concentration through their interest in what they are making, and a sense of self-confidence from a finished product. Often a patient's first renewed contact with reality comes through a bit of modeled clay or a woven rug.

Art therapy also helps patients to regain self-confidence. Its main objective is not the production of masterly finished products but self-expression, which enables patients to free themselves of troubled imaginings through expression in painting. Often a patient's progress can be traced by the change in his depiction of human beings, nature, or abstract ideas. When he is sick, his representations tend to be bizarre and distorted; as he improves, they reflect his being more at peace with himself and the world.

In music therapy, patients get the social experience of participating in bands, orchestras, choruses, and group sings. Also, as a soloist, a patient may be helped to revive an old musical skill or to learn a new one. The wordless self-expression made possible by music, the emotional lift it gives, the opportunity to produce sounds of beauty, gaiety, or inspiration cooperatively, or to give pleasure to others by playing an instrument or singing, all further mental health.

Social, folk, or square dancing is taught in many hospitals, to provide activity, recreation, and doing something with others. A few hospitals having specially trained dance therapists use dancing more profoundly as a form of nonverbal psychotherapy. Patients too sick at first to express themselves in words are enabled to express themselves in bodily movements and so become readied for other therapies. Abnormally self-centered mental invalids, through rhythm, movement, and touch, become cooperative members of a dance group.

For those patients who can profit by it, reading under expert direction may also be a kind of treatment. They learn library work, flower culture, teaching, or writing, and acquire new interests through carefully selected courses of reading.

Since attendance at religious services is a well-established habit for most Americans, hospitals hold Catholic and Protestant services on Sundays, and in localities where there are a number of Jews, a rabbi holds services on Friday evenings or Saturdays, and on Jewish holidays. Some hospitals have resident chaplains who are specially trained for work with mental patients and are available for individual counseling on religious problems with both patients and their families.

If your relative is elderly, he will benefit by "remotivation" or group conversation activity, used in most hospitals for both newly admitted older persons and long-time patients of any age. It consists of a series of small, informal discussion meetings led by an attendant, psychiatric aide, or student nurse. The leader starts these off by presenting some aspect of everyday life that is not related to the patients' emotional difficulties, such as natural history, national holidays, or current events. These group meetings do not purport to be psychotherapy; their aim is pleasurably to rekindle ordinary interests. Verses are read and discussed, and objects such as maps and drawings are used in order to make the subject more real. One group of aging male patients, apparently long uninterested in anything, broke into animated discussion when the leader brought up the topic "dogs."

For recreation, mental hospitals provide dances, concerts, movies, ward picnics, and athletic events. Television and radios are features of today's mental hospitals. Sometimes broadcasts are given within the institution and occasionally to the outside. Ward or hospital newspapers edited by patients, plays, community sings, and many other group activities, differing with different hospitals, are all designed not only to give pleasure to the mentally ill, but also to refit them for life in the community through cooperation with their fellows. Often the public is invited to patients' performances.

Under the supervision of leaders trained to work with groups, patients are encouraged, in short, to participate in all the same kinds of diversions as are enjoyed in the community. Some hospitals, indeed, encourage their patients to use community facilities. But bowling, pool, checkers, chess, basketball, baseball, card games, spelling bees, amateur theatricals, dances, and other forms of group exercise and recreation have even more value for mental patients than for most of us. They help men and women inclined to live too much within themselves to become more normally sociable. By combating idleness enjoyably, they reduce preoccupation with delusions and brooding over real or fancied troubles.

Volunteer workers contribute so much to the pleasure and rehabilitation of mental patients that in a growing number of hospitals their services are coordinated and directed by a special member of the hospital staff. Their unpaid jobs range from helping with music, sports, gardening, dances, entertainment, and occupational therapy, to assisting with medical and social services. Also, they distribute pleasure and comfort items, from cigarettes to television sets, not ordinarily included in hospital budgets. Volunteers have a special value to patients over and above the fun and comforts they provide. Coming in like fresh air from the community, they are a living demonstration that others besides the paid staff of a hospital care about the men and women living there.

Day by day on the wards, too, members of the nursing staff help patients in hundreds of little ways that may add up to recovery. In any good hospital, for instance, tidiness and good grooming are painstakingly encouraged as a means of regaining self-respect. Some hospitals go in for "fashion therapy," that is, volunteer or commercial fashion shows.

Patients who have themselves well in hand are induced to help others, for there is little more curative for self-centered mental invalids than to take some responsibility for their fellow beings. The whole way of life in a mental hospital community, in short, in itself is a generalized form of treatment. Routines and activities are all directed toward helping the patient get well.

CHAPTER **12**

The Family and the Hospital

YOU CAN HELP OR HINDER the hospital in its healing work, as well as make matters easier or more difficult for yourself in your dealings with it.

Some hospitals give out pamphlets or circulars containing details about visiting hours, clothing requirements, switchboard numbers, and other information useful to patients' relatives. If you receive any such printed matter, study it carefully, keep it handy for reference, and follow what it says.

If you do not understand any one of the hospital's regulations, ask to have it explained. At a large hospital, the best way to do this is by writing. A letter will reach the person best qualified to give the information, and will get a more detailed answer than is possible in conversation during busy visiting times or over the telephone. If there is still something not quite clear to you, you can always follow up with a written or verbal inquiry.

Find out at what hours the person who gives information on your patient can be reached over the telephone. Hospitals set definite times when individuals are available to give information by telephone on patients' progress. If you disregard the schedule, the information you get is likely to be about as unsatisfactory as a general hospital's telephonic "The patient is doing as well as can be expected." Don't telephone continually. Changes for better or for worse in mental illness are not always significant; so, with no gain to you, persistent telephone inquiries only bother the hospital's personnel and distract them from the main business of helping patients improve.

Be sure to advise the hospital immediately of any change of address. You will be promptly informed in case of serious physical illness.

When mailing clothing, put your name and address on the package so that it can be acknowledged. For the same reason, it is better not to give any clothing directly to the patient when you visit him in the hospital. Give it to his nurse, or to the supervisor. If the patient, after a visit outside, returns in a change of clothing, inform the hospital so that the garments can be properly marked and won't be lost in the laundry.

Keep your relative supplied with suitable clothing during the full period of his or her stay. It is important both for comfort and for maintaining the self-respect and confidence essential to mental health. A bedraggled evening dress is no more appropriate at breakfast in a mental hospital than at breakfast anywhere else. A mental patient accustomed to wearing clothing in good repair should not be used as a depot for the family's castoffs. On the other hand don't, in your desire to coddle someone used to daily wearing of overalls or house dresses, assemble a dazzling outfit appropriate for a man about town or a debutante. "Suitable" clothing means simply the same kind as the patient has habitually worn.

Don't assume that your relative will be neglected if you do not tip hospital employees. At a private hospital, inquire what the practice is and follow it. At a state hospital, it is best not to give money or presents to any of the personnel. Such gifts, even if offered in all innocence or as a spontaneous expression of appreciation for care and kindness to your patient, embarrass employees because they arouse the suspicion that the family may be seeking favors that cannot be granted. In the best state hospitals there is a wise standing rule against gifts to employees, thus closing the door to favoritism.

Don't ask for or expect special privileges for your relative. In the matter of food, for instance, explain to his physician what the patient likes and doesn't like, but realize that, in a governmental hospital especially, each patient's food quirks and preferences cannot be met. Nor is it always desirable that they should be. Many persons refuse to eat certain foods simply because they are unfamiliar, and overindulgence of food preferences is no better for a mental patient than for a child who refuses to eat this or that. When a special diet is necessary for medical reasons, it is provided under the physician's supervision.

In nearly every state hospital, private rooms cannot be reserved through payment or entreaty. They are occupied by patients who need them for medical reasons, or to further the progress of patients who are beginning to be able to return to the community. Disturbed patients sometimes require solitude, sometimes company; as their individual needs alter, they are shifted from dormitories to private rooms and back again.

Exceptions to a host of details, such as hours of rising or retiring, are also best decided by the hospital authorities. Since they are human beings like the rest of us, the rules they make are not always ideal; some regulations, with changing conditions, have outgrown their usefulness. But hospital routine is determined by experience and by the necessity to achieve a balance between patients' needs and practical problems of staff hours and coverage. The five-day week in mental hospitals, as in general hospitals, has cut down services and activities over weekends. But even when schedules seem to be for the convenience of the staff, they are generally based on the welfare of the patients.

Many families worry about the "regimentation" of a state

hospital. True, each patient must conform to certain hours and mass procedures. He may have more—or less—salt in his food than he likes, or may have to retire earlier than is his habit, but none of these things means that he is disregarded as an individual. His history and behavior, his interests in religion, recreation, and reading, his skills in work and sports are considered and studied. He has personal attention from the employees of the hospital and treatment by various kinds of special therapists. It might take your relative a while to become adjusted to group routine, but fixed schedules are likely to help rather than hinder his progress. Even if they do not, it will do neither him nor you any good to fuss about them.

Feel free to take up with the superintendent or other members of the hospital's staff anything of which you disapprove. That is both your privilege and your obligation. Only, don't start an argument the first time you visit! Wait a while and see whether this or that regulation continues to seem as preposterous to you as it did at first. Always realize that your relative is not only an individual in the hospital but also a member of the hospital group, and that therefore he, too, will benefit by wise blanket provisions.

CHAPTER 13

Letters and Visits

ALTHOUGH THE PRIME RESPONSIBILITY for your patient is in other hands, and although he may be far away from you, never forget that emotionally he remains as involved with his relatives as if he came home every evening. It is therefore important that he have wholesome family contacts. When relatives make a mental patient feel that they are vitally interested in him, and that he is still a loved and accepted member of the family group who will be welcomed back at home as soon as he is well enough to return there, in a very real sense they are partners with the hospital staff in the business of healing.

Perhaps you will be asked to participate in family therapy. Or the hospital or the local mental health association may bring together groups of patients' relatives. If you can meet with such a group, by all means do so. You will get comfort from discovering that your problem, far from being singular or disgraceful, is shared by many other respectable, substantial people. Among those in the same boat you will be able to talk as freely and unself-consciously about your patient's sickness as you can in the hospital. You will learn, reassuringly, that the mental health association is a reliable source of information on the hospital and on present and future difficulties your relative might have. All this will add up to your feeling easier with yourself and your neighbors, and will be reflected in the links you maintain with your relative.

Write to him often and regularly, even though you may have no reply, or replies full of insults. Forlorn, indeed, is the mental hospital patient who receives no mail from his family. Although one member of the family may be the steady correspondent, everyone ought to write at least once in a while.

Make the letters chatty and newsy, and no more self-conscious than if the patient were away on a trip. Except for the natural wish of "I hope you are getting along nicely," or "I hope you are feeling well," which you would write to anyone who is ill, do not refer to his condition. Naturally you will not, either in letters or on visits, crow over all your "grand times," from which the patient is now perforce excluded. Nor will you burden him with accounts of financial or other troubles, about which he can do nothing. These are best poured into the ears of the social worker, the person most likely to help you do something constructive.

Crucial for all concerned are relatives' visits. You can help your patient by the character of your talk and actions with him: through your visits you have it in your power to speed improvement or cause setbacks. You can help the hospital in the smooth carrying out of its general routine and its consistent handling of the patient. You can help yourself, too: families who acquaint themselves with the hospital regulations and who cultivate wise attitudes find visiting pleasanter and more satisfactory than families who try to buck the rules or who behave thoughtlessly.

Some hospitals permit visiting at any time, but most governmental hospitals have visiting days or visiting hours. Make your visits at the prescribed times. The purpose of set visiting periods is not, as many people think, so the hospital can be spruced up and put on its best manners when it has company, but so that busy doctors and ward personnel can devote themselves to their patients instead of being called from their duties to talk with relatives at any and all times. You may be sure that the hospital that you find clean on visiting days is clean the rest of the time, too; and, conversely, the hospital that is ordinarily dirty will also be dirty on visiting days.

During visiting hours patients are kept on the wards or near by. Visitors who come at mealtime may have to wait until the patient gets back from the dining room. If they come on non-visiting days, the patient's treatment may be interrupted or canceled, or he may be deprived of a desired recreation. But every hospital makes exceptions for visitors when they find it a real hardship to come at the scheduled times, when they must travel great distances, or when their patient is seriously ill.

It is so important for the morale of most patients to have their relatives come to see them that some mental health associations provide transportation for families who have no way of getting to the hospital. But visit only as soon—and as often—as the doctor says. In most cases it is desirable to visit frequently. In some, it is best not to go at all. Occasionally staff members, noticing that visits have unfavorable effects on the patient, may advise against them for a period. When it is all right for visits to be resumed, the family is so informed.

Sometimes, on the other hand, the physician asks for more visits than the family finds it agreeable to make. There are patients who feel neglected if their relatives do not visit frequently—which may not prevent them from being ungracious, insulting, and antagonistic whenever the family calls. If the physician tells you to come oftener than you would like, discuss your feelings with him.

Hardest of all, perhaps, for a relative to accept is a doctor's order that he or she only, among all the members of the family, must not go to see the patient. Loving mothers or husbands, especially if their visiting behavior has been faultless, cannot see how their calls at the hospital can possibly be harmful. But the physician, through his understanding of the profound emotions underlying or causing the mental disorder, has come to the conclusion that visits from one or more particular family members tend to stir these up and to cause setbacks. If you are told by the physician that your visits are detrimental, stay away without protest no matter how hurt you feel. When he believes that it is all right for you to visit, he will be only too happy to let you know.

There is no blanket rule as to whether or not young children should be taken to visit a parent or other relative. Find out from the doctor and social worker not only what is permissible, but also what is desirable. They will consider everything that is involved before they advise you. What may be good for the patient may be harmful to the child, or the other way round; or both may be benefited, or both harmed.

Most hospitals have regulations as to the number of visitors at a time. When you arrive you may be given a visitor's pass. So important for patients are community ties that the hospital wants its physicians and social workers to know whose family and friends visit and whose do not.

Ask to see the doctor before you see the patient for the first time, to find out how long the visit should last, and if there are any subjects you ought to avoid in conversation. But then, if your visit seems to upset your relative, leave sooner. If the patient is allowed to go out with you, see that he returns at the specified time.

If you find his behavior worse than when you brought him to the hospital, don't assume that hospitalization has made him sicker. Some mental diseases, like some physical diseases, run a regular course, and the peak of illness may not have been reached at the time he was admitted. If, therefore, he acts more withdrawn or talks more to his voices than he ever did at home, it is not necessarily an indication that he is worse. It may even be a healthy sign that in the permissive hospital atmosphere the pent-up ideas and emotions that caused him to break down are at last being released.

Moreover, in all probability he is acting more abnormally when you visit him than he has acted at any other time during his hospital stay. Mental patients often act up during visits. Knowing that their relatives react more keenly to their behavior than the professionals at the hospital, they tend to go on an emotional orgy when the family comes to call. You may be blamed for having "put me here"; you may be upbraided for neglect. The lovely present into which you have put much tender thought and care may be thrown at your head. Your taste in clothes may be ridiculed, or your behavior in general reviled. The less you show any hurt or grievance at a patient's hostile actions, and the more you realize they are part of his illness, the better for him and for you, and the less likely the performance is to be repeated on your next visit.

Act as natural as possible. Family members often protest, "But I can't act natural." In the last analysis, this doesn't make sense. A normal person *can* act natural. What people really mean is, "I can't make the patient act natural with me." The answer to this is: "Don't try." The hospital is working to make your relative "act natural" again, but this cannot be done overnight. Your part, during visits, is simply to act natural yourself and so far as possible disregard the patient's abnormality. If you have not already done so in letters, tell him all about what is going on in the family, such as job changes, births, engagements, marriages, and deaths. If anything he does makes it impossible for you to be natural, just ignore it. If he asks embarrassing questions, be noncommittal. Even if he seems not to be listening, sit so that he can see you and hear you. No matter how far away or confused he seems, say nothing about him or his condition that you do not want him to understand. Despite the impression that many mental patients give, they are probably taking in everything that goes on.

Observe, and try to imitate as much as you can, the easy way in which nurses, psychiatric aides, and attendants act with even the most abnormally behaved patients. They are listeners, as attentive as their time permits. They disregard wild utterances and respond to reasonable ones. They calmly act as if the patient were normal, thereby helping him toward normality.

Don't swallow, hook, line, and sinker, everything your patient says about the hospital. Be inwardly skeptical of tales of neglect or punishments. The distorted viewpoint of mental patients gives rise to statements that have little or no relation to the facts. A description of any circumstance that seems very real to your relative may hide only a tiny kernel of truth under a mass of misstatements. Also, frequently, mental patients, like normal folk, just plain lie.

For all the care that may be taken in preparing patients for injections or shock therapy, many of them, because of the very nature of their illness, misinterpret these medical treatments as punishments. Do not let your relative mislead you into thinking that he is being abused when actually he is being treated.

If you have reason to suspect, however, that the patient's accusations are justified, by all means take them up point by point with the physician, supervisor, social worker, or chaplain—or, if necessary, with the superintendent. The best procedure is to write, setting forth the full details of the complaint and giving the patient's full name. Unless you are completely specific, no one in authority can correct the situation.

Sometimes families fail to report a patient's valid complaint for fear that the hospital employee criticized will "take it out" on their relative. This is shortsighted, for the patient will be worse off if the abuse continues unchecked.

Bringing along the kind of gifts you would bring to a patient in any hospital, such as flowers, toilet water, shaving lotion, books, magazines, games, is an indication of interest and affection that is always in order. Find out the hospital's policy about food treats. Usually hospitals prefer that food brought in be the kind that either can be eaten during the visit or is not perishable, although some hospitals provide refrigerators for patients' personal use. Never bring any alcoholic beverages to the hospital.

Be friendly and courteous with other patients, but refrain from asking them personal questions such as who they or their relatives are, what is their job, business or profession, or why they are in the hospital. Don't gape at any celebrities who may be among the patients. Above all, do not question other patients for the purpose of getting an inside report on your own relative's behavior. Not only might you upset them, but the information you get will be valueless. If you approach them with "The doctor says my Mary makes trouble on the ward. Is it really true?" they may answer anything at all, true or false, to stop your interruption of their daydreams or to be dramatic. At any rate, you cannot count on well-considered answers, based on facts, from the mentally ill.

Don't act as a go-between for patients. Do not, at their request, telephone to their relatives or to the police to take them out because they are "perfectly all right." Do not take any letters to mail. If your relative, or any other patient, is so insistent that you are afraid to refuse, take the letter, but tell him at the same time, "I shall give it to the nurse," and do so. Never lie to your relative or to any other patient.

Patients who think their families do not want to have them back—for instance, old people—sometimes act sicker in the hospital than their condition warrants, because this gives them the unconscious face-saving "Well, after all, I really belong here." Let your relative know that you will be happy when he can be home again for good. Talk about what you will all do together again, but do not make him overly impatient to return. Make no statements about taking him out of the hospital beyond the assurance "Just as soon as the doctor says it's all right."

Ask the staff members who keep you informed about the patient what, in turn, they would like to know from you. Your observations on changes in behavior, after you have visited your patient or he has visited you at home, for example, can play a vital part in further decisions on treatment.

If for one reason or another it is impossible for you to visit, find out from the hospital whether you can reassure your relative of your interest in him by means of telephone calls, how often it is advisable to call, whether at regular times or unexpectedly, and just how and when it is best to reach him.

For the sake of your own patient and his ward or hospital associates, keep your emotions rigidly under control whenever you visit. If you feel that you are reaching the breaking point, leave before it comes. Exactly the same principles that guide you on a visit to a general hospital, a college, a convent, an army camp, or a children's summer camp—courtesy, restraint, consideration, truthfulness, and respect for authority—should guide you in your visits to a mental hospital.

CHAPTER 14

Returning the Patient to the Community

JUST WHEN YOUR RELATIVE will be able to return full-time to the community, and under what arrangements, will depend of course upon his condition and progress. But it will also depend on your readiness to absorb him into the family again, the policy of the hospital, and the availability of community facilities to give him emotional support and medical aftercare. All modern hospitals, you may be sure, go upon the principle that anyone able to manage outside a hospital ought not be detained within it.

Nevertheless, taking a patient out of a hospital too soon can be as dangerous as bringing him there too late. If you take your relative's word, instead of the hospital's, as to his readiness for discharge, you may be inviting tragedy. For instance, a formerly depressed patient may assure you he is now happy and convince you that he is better. He is; but it is just when a depression starts to lift and the patient is on the upgrade and seems cheerful that suicide is most likely to occur. Many families have discovered this to their sorrow within twenty-four hours after they had acted "against medical advice" by removing a "well" relative from a hospital. Or a patient who has improved sufficiently to live comfortably under the protection of an institution may seem cured to himself and to you, yet break down again completely when he has to take his place in the outside world.

The pressure brought to bear on families to "take me out of here" is often almost intolerable. Senile patients, directly or indirectly accusing the children they have reared—and, if they are women, borne—of ingratitude, are especially wily in playing on feelings of guilt for not keeping them at home. Often their very illness causes them to give heart-rending reports of abuse.

Let the doctor know that you are eager and willing to have your relative back at home as soon as possible. He may thus leave sooner than if the hospital staff thinks it has to reckon with a rejecting or indifferent family that will complicate the patient's fitting into community life again.

But keep your patient in the hospital—or take him out of it— not a day later or a day sooner than the staff say is advisable. Their professional experience makes them the best judge, and they will base their opinion on that. If the doctor believes your patient is still too ill to be responsible for his words or actions, you won't convince him to the contrary by saying, "John says he wouldn't do those awful things again"; or, "I know him so well, and I know he's himself again." Your love for one mental patient is no substitute for the doctor's trained, objective observation of thousands of them over the years.

Families are especially loath to accept the advice of physicians in private hospitals when they recommend some continued hospitalization for improved patients; money-grabbing motives are suspected. On the other hand, relatives also accuse state hospital superintendents of being "hardhearted" in sending patients out too soon. Neither is true. The facts are that private hospital staffs tend to recommend hospitalization for as long as they believe the patient can benefit by treatment, while the staffs of overcrowded state hospitals, under pressure to clear beds, tend to send them out, perhaps with continuing medication, as soon as they are well enough to get along.

Dramatic and rapid improvements in mental illness often occur when an organic cause of the disease—such as meningitis—is successfully treated, or after drug or shock treatment. A sharp change for the better in such cases, however, does not mean that the patient is "all well." As aftercare is needed in surgical cases, so psychotherapy and other rehabilitating treatments are needed in mental cases, even though the outward signs of the disease may have disappeared.

The better the hospital, the less abrupt will be the released patients' resumption of responsibility in the community. From the very beginning of their stay, and throughout it, long or short, in many ways they are gradually prepared for leaving. They have increasing freedom and responsibilities within the hospital. They go home overnight or for weekends, and on outside excursions with their families or with volunteer workers. Vocational counselors keep them talking and thinking about the kind of employment they will have, and they have practice in working in the hospital. They may assist with the care of the sicker patients, or fill various hospital jobs that require a high degree of concentration and alertness. Then shortly before they leave they review with a physician and a social worker the situation leading up to the illness. Problems they are likely to meet are discussed with them at a staff meeting. The family, too, is briefed on possible difficulties. Immediate occupational and recreational plans are made in a give-and-take discussion between patients and the physicians and social workers, and if they have not already been in the picture, perhaps with State Vocational Rehabilitation Agency counselors too. Possibilities of embarrassing situations are anticipated, talked over, and perhaps acted out for practice in coping with them.

One way of bridging the gap between the shelter of the hospital and the free-for-all world, called family or foster care, is being adopted by a growing number of states. Family care is the hospital's placement of medically selected patients in homes carefully chosen and supervised by social workers. The routine, monotony, and relative impersonality of the institution are replaced by the personal warmth and intimacy of family life, which often includes church and other community participation. The patient is gradually prepared for life with his own family again.

Some patients live in family care in order to get schooling or vocational training for which there are no facilities in their home communities. Some who are able to work for wages or for full or partial maintenance do so; others have board paid for them by the hospital. Family-care patients may be virtually adopted by the families with whom they live, as grandmother or teen-age son or uncle; and for as long as they are in the home they get the same kind of interest and affection as if they were real relatives.

At its best, family care is more than a pleasant way of living; it is a form of therapy. The warm influence of family life, the patient's participation in it, the acceptance of his peculiarities outside the hospital, and the day-by-day challenge of getting along intimately with others in ordinary surroundings act as powerful healing forces.

If the hospital recommends a period of family care, agree to it gladly and do not feel that it means something must be wrong with your own household. Many a patient "impossible" in his own home has blossomed as a pleasant member of someone else's. And having learned how to live with a family, he is more likely to live well with his own family again.

Nor need you be anxious about the conditions under which your relative will live in family care. Everywhere such homes must meet certain standards of cleanliness and comfort; and caretakers must be kindly and responsible. It is the experience of hospitals that the likelihood of patients' being overindulged by their caretakers is greater than the likelihood of their being exploited. The board money paid by states for family care is modest, and the main motive of caretakers—most of them middle-aged women whose children are grown and whose houses are empty—is a motherly desire to "do" for someone.

"Halfway houses" are a more recent development. Where the handful of them exists, patients who no longer need hospital supervision can live while they work in the community. Halfway houses are very much like residence clubs and usually charge comparable rates. Ingenious reductions of rates may be made, however, as an encouragement to residents to become fully contributing members of the community. The man or woman in charge of a halfway house, though not a psychiatrist, usually has some kind of background for helping members of a group to live pleasantly with one another, and for knowing when it is advisable to call for psychiatric help. Many residents of halfway houses continue to be under psychiatric care in private offices or outpatient clinics until they are able to live on their own.

All states have legal provision for a period variously called "provisional discharge," "conditional discharge," "conditional release," "trial visit," "extended visit," or "convalescent leave" to precede discharge. Such periods vary in length from three to twelve months and may be extended if necessary. Some hospitals still call them "parole"; this is an unfortunate term, for it has criminal connotations, but the principle remains good.

During the period of trial visit, or whatever its equivalent is called, the patient usually lives outside the hospital, but is more or less under its watchful eye through a worker at one of its outpatient clinics or at a community clinic. If the patient lives near enough to report periodically to the hospital, he might be expected to do so.

A social worker or a nurse on the hospital staff or a public health nurse will probably visit your home from time to time to see whether everything is going along as expected. Your relative's ability to live in everyday surroundings during the trial period is the basis for determining whether he shall be discharged or returned to the hospital.

In states that have the better mental health laws, both trial visit and discharge of patients who have not entered the hospital voluntarily or informally are left entirely to the decision of the hospital. In some states discharge is subject to the decision of a special board, and in a few it can be effected only by a court. Everywhere—provided he has a place to go and is no longer a danger to himself or others—it is easier to get a patient out of a mental hospital than to get him in. For the first time in history discharges from mental hospitals are exceeding new admissions. Many patients who might formerly have had to have long hospital stays have been able to go home very soon after admission; usually, however, such patients must continue with their medication under the supervision of a psychiatrist or family physician.

CHAPTER 15

Back Home with the Family

YOUR RELATIVE MAY BE provisionally or fully discharged to live with you at home. No matter how happy you are to have him back, the situation is never simple. Whenever anyone has been away from home for a while, the family has had to adjust to carrying on without him. When he returns, it has to readjust. The readjustment may be as major as having to quit a satisfying job taken during the emergency to return to housekeeping, or as minor as giving up a temporarily unused closet that came in so handy for storage. The important thing is to recognize such frustrations for what they are; then you will not take them out in irritation against the returned patient.

As, in a good hospital, he has been prepared to return home, so the family has also been prepared to receive him. But here again you may find useful the pamphlet mentioned in Chapter 3, *Helping a Mental Patient at Home,* available from Mental Health Associations.

Some families expect too much of their former patient. They think he should be "cured," or "act just as he did before he got sick." Remember that doctors rarely use the word "cured";

what they say is "recovered" or "improved." Your relative may be far from cured, and not even fully recovered, yet still get on very well outside the hospital.

Other families with a member just out of a mental hospital feel like some families with a new baby—helpless, frightened, and likely to exaggerate every little symptom. A family doctor, public health nurse, or social worker is the aide of the apprehensive relatives of such mental patients. Any time during a trial visit that you are dubious about your relative's fitness to get along at home, report what worries you and find out what ought to be done. If the hospital does not have social workers available in your community, telephone to it, by long distance if necessary. You may be advised that you have no cause for concern, or you may receive suggestions on how to deal with what is happening, or you may be told that your relative had better be seen by one of the hospital psychiatrists. The appointment will probably be at the hospital's outpatient clinic if it has one, or at the hospital itself if it has not.

Each homecoming patient is different of course, and the regimen that works well with one may not be suitable for another. Everyone—ex-mental patient or not—can stand only so much stress before he breaks down; the danger point varies widely with different individuals. Your relative's physician will tell you what kind of strain is to be avoided, if possible, because in his judgment it is likely to precipitate a setback; he will also advise you on the way of life likely to be best for the patient at this point. Aside from such individual variations, treat your convalescent as nearly as possible as you do the other members of the family.

Bear in mind that the situation now is very different from what it was when your relative entered the hospital. Then he was sick, driven by distorted ideas, and no more responsible for his behavior than a cripple is responsible for limping. Now you can assume that, though perhaps he has not quite regained his full mental and emotional strength, he is no longer an invalid. His treatments at the hospital should have given him understanding of himself, and increasingly he can be held responsible for his actions.

Therefore, do not pamper your newly returned patient. He should not be petted after a tantrum or encouraged to withdraw to his room whenever there is a distasteful caller. Most parents know the difficulties of retraining a youngster who has become spoiled during a period of illness. Mental patients become similarly accustomed to a certain amount of care and protection in a hospital. Just as the convalescent child learns, with wise guidance, to live happily again without being waited on hand and foot, so the convalescent mental patient, if he is not overindulged by his loving family, can readapt to home and social life.

The sooner and more easily you let your convalescent resume his normal place in your household, the better. Post him on the neighborhood news so he won't feel left out of conversations. If you are a party-giving family you might celebrate your relative's return home by a dinner or tea in his honor. Include him naturally in whatever are your habitual family activities—churchgoing, visits to the neighbors, or shopping expeditions.

Don't, however, plan too much entertainment. Far from cheering him up, by taking him into gay, noisy groups you may upset him and cause him to withdraw unhealthily into his shell. If at all possible in a crowded household, let him occasionally be alone.

If the hospital or family doctor has prescribed continued medication, see that your relative takes it no matter how well he seems. Regular medication is as necessary to keep some mental illnesses under control as, for instance, some drugs are to control diabetes. Should the medicine prescribed for your relative cost more than you can afford, discuss this with your family doctor, the hospital social worker, or a social worker associated with either the Family Service Agency or public welfare department in your community. Arrangements can often be made to get drugs at reduced prices, or, if necessary, free.

Never suggest tranquilizing drugs or sleeping pills, or attempt to procure them unless a doctor has prescribed them. Don't proffer "a good stiff drink," or other means of escape from the reality that he must face. If he takes a trip with the idea of getting away from it all, it only defers the moment when he must fit in with things as they are. As sheer recreation, however, a trip may be as desirable for former mental patients as for anyone else. In no case force your relative to do anything because you think it's good for him. Respect his inclinations, unless they involve breaking a state regulation such as prohibition of a mental patient's driving a car or piloting a plane. Find out from the hospital what the regulations are. In any case, persons under heavy doses of tranquilizers are unsafe drivers or pilots because of drowsiness. When your relative's wishes seem unreasonable consult your own or the hospital's physician or social worker.

For a while, however, chart your relative's day so that the change from the hospital regimen does not come too abruptly. Help him find wholesome occupations—not necessarily for pay—such as gardening, reading, or sports. But if he is not yet earning, see that he has enough pocket money so that he does not feel dependent and humiliated by having to ask for every little thing he wants.

Some communities have sheltered workshops where the mentally and emotionally handicapped can earn without the usual on-the-job competition and pressures. In many communities there are social clubs for men and women recently out of mental hospitals. Usually these are operated by mental health associations. Membership in such clubs helps ex-patients to become part of a group and to enjoy contacts and friendships with others with whom they feel comfortable. Under the guidance of professional leaders, the clubs help those whose emotions may still be a bit shaky to overcome fears about making new friends, to develop new interests and hobbies, to discover what the community affords in recreational facilities and opportunities for civic participation, and sometimes to prepare for or even find a job. Ask your local Mental Health Association or a social worker whether there is a sheltered workshop or such a club in your community, and if there is, encourage your relative to join it.

In those larger plans involving vocation, be guided above all by the doctor and perhaps the social worker or state Vocational Rehabilitation Counselor, or the state employment agency's specialist on the handicapped. They can gauge, better than you or your relative, how much responsibility he is now not only able to take but also should. It might be better, for instance, for someone who has always had his own business, to give that up and work for someone else; yet, for a former executive to work as a delivery man might be more destructive to his self-confidence than to have no job at all.

Employers vary greatly in their readiness to take on former mental patients, so whether or not your relative should be frank about his hospitalization has to be played by ear. If there is a sizable gap in his work history, it might be less of a strain to take the chance of explaining it than to conceal why it occurred. Some employment experts believe that ex-mental patients have the best opportunity to get jobs with small firms, where hiring is more informal than in large ones, and an array of forms does not need to be filled in; but there is really no rule about this, and a large firm may actually be the more receptive to those who have been mentally ill. Employers who openly admit doubts and fears about employing former patients, yet who may be persuaded to try, tend to be more likely prospects than others who proclaim that they have none, but act contrary to their assertions. There is only one certain, highly encouraging fact. In a tight labor market, if your relative has a needed skill, he will have absolutely no trouble finding a job.

Moreover, with the persistent, increasing public-education activities of mental health associations, there are not nearly so many employers set against employing former mental patients as most people think.

Inside the home a mother may not yet be ready to take up the complex duties of running a household and caring for her children. In such cases the social worker can give practical help as well as guidance. For example, she may know where to get a professional homemaker—someone who will take over one hundred per cent, or someone who will simply carry out orders, relieving yet not replacing the housewife, as best suits the former patient's needs.

With the world, as well as with your relative, act as if he had returned from any other hospital. On the one hand don't harp upon his illness; on the other, don't self-consciously avoid references to it, or keep him from renewing old contacts because you fear the unhappy events that led to his hospitalization will all come back to him. If he suspects that you want to cover up what has happened, he is likely to become worried and anxious.

The main thing to bear in mind during trial visits and the period after discharge is that many mental patients are people so sensitive that they have retreated into a dream world rather than endure the hurts of life. Restored to reality, they still need understanding, kindness, acceptance, and sympathy—not the crying-on-the-shoulder type of sympathy, but the constructive kind that helps them maintain their self-confidence and enables them squarely to shoulder their responsibilities once more.

CHAPTER 16

Relapses and Readmissions

THE NOTION THAT NO ONE who has been mentally ill can ever be quite "right" again dies hard but is false. Though many patients well enough to leave mental hospitals still have some aftermath of illness, the number of others who become fully and permanently restored to usefulness in the community nowadays gives the lie to age-old superstitions and suspicions.

Nevertheless, over one-third of those admitted to public and private mental hospitals or to the psychiatric services of general hospitals have had one or more prior hospitalizations. If your relative is one of them, do not let his relapses plunge you into gloom. Readmission is not evidence that he must spend the rest of his life in and out of a hospital, for any one may be the last.

Don't assume that the patient left the hospital too soon if he seems worse at home than the last time you were with him. Readjustment to home life is always difficult after hospitalization; this is true even of patients who have had a relatively brief stay in a general hospital. In addition, during the period he has spent in a mental hospital, home has seemed very glamorous.

The realities of little inconveniences and little frictions may, therefore, come to him as somewhat of a shock and tend to give him a temporary setback.

What might also happen toward the end of a trial visit is that, without realizing that he is fearful of burning the bridges to the more protective hospital, he may begin to feel shaky and, in consequence, act upset and abnormal again. If he goes back to the hospital, his second stay there may be shorter than his first, and his third shorter still.

Let the hospital, or private-practice psychiatrist, or family physician, or the treatment team that has cared for him throughout his illness decide whether your patient should be readmitted. Families who were reluctant to recognize mental illness when it struck and delayed too long in calling for help, sometimes act liked burned children and tend to be too critical of returned relatives. Remember that few of us could meet the test of absolute mental health. Very likely your relative who has been discharged retains some peculiar mannerisms, exaggerated fears, or over-conscientious scruples. So have we all our peculiarities and mental quirks!

Readmission does not always involve returning to the hospital full-time. There may be provisions for day or night hospitalization at the hospital or an extension of it in the community, or a community mental health center, or a general hospital.

Explore all the community resources for keeping your relative on an even keel and preventing the need for readmission. "Supportive therapy" can be very important in this. As its name suggests, it has encouragement and morale-building as its main objective. With professional skill and understanding, but without deep psychiatric probing, the therapist helps to strengthen self-confidence possibly weakened by rebuffs from friends or prospective employers, to allay renewed or fresh anxieties, or to reinforce insights gained at the hospital. The therapist may be a psychiatrist, a general physician, a clergyman, a clinical psychologist, or a social worker. The local Mental Health Association can guide you to who is most appropriate and available.

Practically everywhere psychiatric clinics have long waiting lists; and in some sections of the country, especially in sparsely settled regions, there is no nearer place than the state hospital to get psychiatric help. It is quite possible that your relative will be reluctant to go there. Former mental patients are often terrified at the thought of going anywhere near the hospital for fear they may not "get out" again. If you have been truthful with your relative from the beginning, you will have little difficulty in convincing him that a checkup is a preventive measure, and that everyone concerned is interested in keeping him out of the hospital, not in putting him back. If you have made the mistake of deceiving him during the acute stage of his illness, you can make up for it somewhat by confessing that you lied to him through ignorance, that you have learned better just as he learned much through his experience with mental illness, and that you are being honest now. Never threaten return to the hospital as a punishment for "not behaving."

Drugs prescribed by a psychiatrist or family physician may also prevent the readmission of many discharged patients. This does not mean that your relative will necessarily be kept on the same medicine he had been taking before. The doctor may continue him on a drug for some time and then change to another, which may bring about better results. Or dosage may be reduced, or a drug stopped for a while, for the purpose of discovering whether the patient can now get along with less medication or none. Realize, however, that some former mental hospital patients need to be kept on drugs for a considerable period of time, even as long as several years. One of the most frequent causes of relapses today is failure to take the prescribed medication. It is impossible to overemphasize the importance of doing everything you can to ensure that your relative explicitly follows medical instructions. Do not let him talk you into accepting his discontinuation or reduction of his drug dosage because he says things like "I don't need it any more," or "It makes me too sleepy," or "It makes my mouth feel dry"; insist that he consult the doctor.

Although most readmissions could be prevented if communities had more facilities for helping former mental patients to stay well and if everyone made it easier for them to fit in again to their jobs and homes, relapses are not "caused" solely by "something that happened." Some of us bear up under a load of troubles and disturbances; others break down under relatively trivial strains. Though it is true that agitated and panicky reactions by relatives at the first signs of abnormal behavior may precipitate a relapse, while calm and sensible handling of the situation may avert it, the best medical care and wisest procedures cannot always prevent the necessity for rehospitalization. Something within the individual may make him susceptible to the disorder, just as some persons are subject to flu, and whatever precautions they take, have recurrent attacks of the malady. Also, some mental diseases are chronic, like chronic arthritis, in which there may be years without symptoms or discomfort and then, for no apparent reason, a sudden flareup.

During the periods between disorders, your relative may be normal and should be treated as normal. These intervals may last for years at a time; even among those types of mental illnesses most likely to recur there are many instances of patients whose first attack was their last.

CHAPTER 17

Continued Care

NOT ALL PATIENTS ADMITTED to even the finest hospitals recover, any more than all patients admitted to good general hospitals recover. Some have to spend the rest of their lives as hospital patients.

Those who must have continued care fall into several groups.

There are bedridden infirmary patients. Among them are infirm old people; victims of severe crippling diseases such as those of the nervous system or arthritis; and those with other physical ailments that would make them require hospital care even if they were mentally well.

There are patients who did not respond well, or respond no further, to treatment. Although they may be better than when they came to the hospital, they are still on a level that makes it impossible for them to get along in the community.

Another group of continued-care patients consists of those men and women who entered the hospital quite sick, but progressed, step by step, under treatment until they reached a relatively high plateau. Although not quite well enough to enter the outside world, they make good institutional citizens. Some are "afraid" to leave the hospital and cannot be induced to do so. Many feel a proprietary interest in the institution and are proud of the nurses, psychiatric aides, attendants, and associates on their "good" wards. Occupational and recreational programs are especially arranged for them. Often they do skilled work in the housekeeping department and sometimes in offices; typically they are on open wards and on dance and party lists.

A number of hospitals, though maintaining technical responsibility for old people who may or may not be bedridden but are too feeble and confused to take care of themselves, transfer them to nursing homes or boarding homes in the community after their acute symptoms have subsided. This is fine, if such homes are good. But if your relative is aged, look carefully into whether he would not still benefit by psychiatric care or whether he is just being "dumped" in an inferior institution to make more hospital beds available for younger patients.

An appallingly large number of patients in nearly every mental hospital would be well enough to be discharged if there were someone to take the responsibility of looking after them. Many are old people, but some are working patients. Deaths in their families, adverse economic conditions, housing problems, shortage of staff to prepare them for discharge, and, above all, lack of community facilities that could provide some care and supervision swell their number. Family care, the placement of selected patients in supervised homes, is one excellent way of reducing it; the patients get the satisfactions of home life, and the hospital has beds freed.

No matter how remote you regard the possibility of recovery, never abandon a patient. Unnecessary heartbreak occurs when families consider their relations with a mental patient a closed chapter. It is pitiful to see mental hospital inhabitants who have not had a caller for perhaps twenty years groom themselves and wait hopefully on visiting day. Often the fact that someone related by blood or marriage still cares is the only thing in life to which a patient clings—and this holds good even if he displays apparent indifference or antagonism to anyone and everyone. If the regular letter writer and visitor in your family dies, be sure that someone else takes over.

On the other hand, don't have the wrong kind of "interest" in your patient. If he leaves the grounds without permission, comes home, and begs you to keep him there, report it at once to the hospital.

Most hospitals concentrate their efforts on the more recently admitted patients. But in the best ones, continued-care patients are not merely housed, fed, and clothed. Periodic physical check-ups are made, and every month or six weeks each patient has a personal interview with his doctor. He is asked how he is getting along, and his program is adjusted in accordance with his interests and capacities. There are hospitals where continued-care patients are periodically put back on active treatment to see whether it might help them now. When a state institutes or enlarges family care or some other kind of community-centered project, groups of continued-care patients are combed for eligibles. Very occasionally a patient who has been institutionalized for a long while reacts to family care like the old lady who complained of "having to go upstairs to the bathroom"; at her own request she was returned to the hospital. Far more frequently, hospital old-timers blossom in their new homes. Similarly, when a new therapy is developed it is used on continued-care patients who might benefit by it, often with strikingly good results.

Though the great majority of recoveries occur within the first few weeks or months of hospitalization, some patients who have been hospitalized for many, many years are also discharged. "While there's life there's hope" is as applicable to mental as to body ills.

CHAPTER 18

There's More You Can Do

WHATEVER THE OUTCOME of a mental illness in your family, you will have been through one of the most difficult and trying experiences any human being can have; indeed, the family of a mental invalid may suffer more than the patient. It is only natural, therefore, not a sign of weakness, if you feel shaken by your ordeal. Its aftermath in you may be anything from tenseness, self-doubt, anxiety about the future, and tormenting yourself with what you might or might not have done to contribute to the illness, to crying out "Why should this happen to me?"

In order to live again successfully with yourself, your relative, and your fellow men, however, you will have to set your own emotional house in order. You might have the insight and faith to do this unaided. But if not, do not hesitate to get help in regaining your equilibrium from your clergyman or family physician, a Family Service agency, or a psychiatrist.

Probably before mental illness came close to you, you had thought very little about what the mentally ill are like. But each life experience that touches us personally broadens our interests and sympathies, and now, doubtless, you have a new concern in the problems of mental illness and their solution.

Perhaps this takes the form of wanting to do some immediate kindness for patients in mental hospitals, either by way of personal service or of donations of things that will brighten their lives, like chintz curtains for a dreary dining room, or Christmas and birthday presents for the lonely men and women who either have no friends or relatives in the world outside the hospital, or are ignored by those they had.

The best way to carry out such generous impulses is through an organization with a well-set-up program of volunteer service in mental hospitals. Among such organizations are mental health associations and the American Red Cross. Not only do they recruit and train volunteers, but also they work in the most effective possible way with hospitals, which make the ultimate decisions as to what volunteer services or suggested items to be donated are needed and practicable.

Many hospitals are so aware of the value of outsiders' contributions to the happiness and welfare of patients that a special staff member, usually called Director or Supervisor of Volunteers, is assigned to work with those offering their services. To continued-care patients, volunteers bring even more than the joy that visits and little attentions give any shut-in; the inspiriting contact with the community that they provide often helps a patient likely to become sicker to hold the line he has reached. To more recently admitted patients, volunteer supplementation of an overloaded staff may mean the difference between a shorter and a longer hospital stay, indeed, even between recovering mental health and remaining mentally ill!

By acting through an established volunteer program, whether you are a woman or a man, you will find a wide range of possible assignments from which to choose what is most congenial to you and by which you can best serve patients. You might assist with recreation and athletics; with a variety of craftwork or in connection with the library; with cooking, sewing, gardening, or shopwork. You might lead patients' clubs, or special hobby groups like bird watchers, music lovers, stamp collectors, or fly tiers. Giving time to individual patients, you might write letters, read aloud, play two-handed games, or attend to shopping needs. If you are trained as a beautician, your skill will be welcomed; many mental hospital beauty parlors are staffed by volunteer operators.

Even if you cannot or do not want to give the time required for a regular assignment, there are, nevertheless, some kinds of volunteer services you can give. You might work with organizations that give occasional large parties in the hospital, or hold special events. You might be part of a group that supplies patients with year-round needs—as well as Christmas gifts—such as magazines, books, and little comfort items like toilet articles and cigarettes; although most of us take such amenities for granted, they are unlikely to be included in hospital budgets. Or you might join with others in raising money to provide a substantial gift for a whole ward, such as attractive, comfortable day-room furniture, a record player, or a TV set.

Indeed, patients have needs that you can help to fill without stirring out of your own home. Among them are cakes for birthday parties or homemade clothing items for those who cannot wear stock sizes.

If the hospital with which you are concerned is one of the few that have no volunteer program, or is not in process of establishing one, you have no recourse but to offer to serve on your own. Be sure to clear with the superintendent or whomever he designates, however, anything you want to do or give. Your very interest may stimulate him to take steps to get a volunteer department for his hospital.

But perhaps your desire to better the lot of the mentally ill is not satisfied by direct service to them. You have the urge to do something constructive about the broader aspects of mental illness.

Here, too, you can be most effective as a member of an organized group, strengthening and reinforcing its efforts with your support. Join the mental health association in your state or local community. As an affiliate of the National Association for Mental Health, it is dedicated to a comprehensive fight against mental illness and to the over-all improvement of mental health.

This national association sponsors and stimulates research into the causes, treatment, and prevention of nervous and mental disorders and advises government bureaus, state agencies, and community organizations on problems affecting mental health. To improve standards for the care and treatment of the mentally ill, it has helped universities and medical students to provide competently trained workers for the mental health field. It has a careers program to inform young people about vocational opportunities in mental health and thereby to increase the number of new workers entering the field. If you are high school or college age, or have children of those ages, or know other young people whom you might influence, obtain these pamphlets: *Mental Health Jobs Today and Tomorrow,* Public Affairs Committee, Inc., 381 Park Avenue South, New York, N. Y. 10016, 25 cents; *Nursing Careers in Mental Health,* U.S. Government Printing Office, Washington, D.C. 20402, 15 cents. Write also to the National Association for Mental Health, 10 Columbus Circle, New York, N. Y. 10019, for a list of publications on career possibilities. For all the many kinds of mental health specialists, demand far exceeds supply.

If your community does not have a comprehensive mental health center, use your influence as a citizen to get one started, so that the very young and the very old, the mildly sick and the severely sick, all will have a chance to be treated promptly and consistently without having to go away. The procedure is for the community to study its mental health needs and submit a plan for meeting them to the state mental health authority. If it fits in with the state's coordinated plan and is approved, the state in turn applies for approval from the National Institute of Mental Health and a share of federal funds to support the project. But however well financed, a community mental health center can be effective only if the community itself is involved, and its citizens do not merely initiate it but continually follow up on its adaptations to local needs. Here, again, you can exercise the most power through affiliation with the National Association for Mental Health. For over two generations its branches in many states, counties, and cities have acted as clearinghouses of information on all phases of mental health. Mental health associations carry on programs of public education on mental health and mental illness. On the basis of surveys of state hospitals, they have encouraged the public to support legislative efforts to change institutions for lifelong care into true treatment hospitals, and they have influenced state legislatures to remedy unsatisfactory conditions.

It is not so very long ago in world history that the mentally ill were treated worse than captive animals—flogged, bedded on filthy straw, chained, and exhibited for a fee. Today, as a result of the work of medical and social reformers, of investigators who have exposed unsatisfactory conditions, and of continual public pressure, even our worst state hospitals are better than the best of them fifty years ago. Since the end of World War II, especially, many flagrant abuses have been done away with; dirt, brutality, and disgracefully antiquated, substandard buildings have largely disappeared. But there is more, much more, still to be done. In too many so-called hospitals there remain wards that are essentially asylums: patients are given kindly care but little or no active treatment.

Nearly every state hospital is overcrowded; all are understaffed. Most struggle along on budgets ridiculously inadequate compared with the budgets of general hospitals. Nevertheless, some states take conspicuously better care of their mentally sick citizens than others do. Usually the reason behind inferior state hospitals is lack of money and the consequent difficulty of retaining a competent staff, frustrated because they cannot apply what they know. Sometimes it is political patronage. Unqualified employees, uncertain of their tenure, do not develop hospitals to the level of those staffed by men and women who are selected for their abilities to perform their duties and not for their services to The Party, and who are interested in making plans for betterment because they know they will remain to carry them out. Use your power as a member of a mental health association to get politics out of mental hospitals and the merit system in.

Such an organized group can also exert its influence on the side of any proposed legislation that will improve the lot of the mentally ill, relieve overcrowding in state hospitals, increase the percentage of cures, or decrease the number of necessary new admissions. Proposed laws may be for increased appropriations for state hospitals; for community psychiatric clinics where early symptoms of mental illness can be detected and treated, and a real breakdown prevented; for family care; or for up-to-date admission procedures. Remember always that community facilities, state hospitals, and state laws pertaining to mental illness are only as good as the people of the state demand that they be. You, who have been initiated into the service of mental patients by experience, can be an effective crusader.

Index

121

Music therapy, 80–81

National Association for Mental
Health, 118, 119
National Association of Private Psy-
chiatric Hospitals, 48
National Directory of Homemaker
Services, 75
National Institute of Mental Health,
119
Nervous breakdown, 16, 17, 19, 24
New York State, 59, 60
"Nonprotesting" admission to mental
hospital, 57
Nurses, 73, 83
Nursing Careers in Mental Health,
118
Nursing home, 32

Occupational therapy, 80, 105
Open wards, 30, 76
Outpatient clinics, 28, 50

Paresis, 35
Parole, 100
Parting from patient, 65
Part-time hospitalization, 30–31, 50
Pastoral institute, 23
Penicillin, 35
Persecution, 24–25, 56
Play therapy, 36–37
Politics in mental hospitals, 51, 73,
120
Priest, 22
Private rooms in mental hospitals,
86
Privileges for patients, 86
Pyschiatric interview, 70
Psychiatric services in general hospi-
tals, 28
Psychiatrist, 22
Psychoanalysis, 36
Psychodrama, 38
Psychological examination, 70
Psychologist, 70, 71
Psychotherapy, 35–36, 98
Public Affairs Committee, 118
Punishment of patients, 73, 75, 93,
119

Rabbi, 22
"Railroading" into mental hospitals,
54–55
Reading therapy, 81
Readmission to mental hospital, 108–
111
Recreation activities, 82
Re-employment, 106
Regulations, hospital, 84
Rehabilitation, 102–107
Relapses, 108–111
Religious services, 81
Remedies, amateur, 24
Remotivation therapy, 81–82
Reputability of mental hospitals, 48
Retardation, 54
Role-playing, 38

Schizophrenia, 35
Seeking help, 21
Selecting a mental hospital, 46–49
Semiopen wards, 76
Senile patients, 97
Shock treatment, 34, 35, 98
Social Security, 29, 49
Social worker, 23, 31–32, 47, 65, 70,
71, 74, 91, 93, 100, 103, 107
State hospitals, 50–52
"Stigma" of mental illness, 17, 41
Suicide, 21–22, 44, 64, 96
Supportive therapy, 109
Surgery, 35
Symptoms of mental illness, 19–21
Syphilis, 35, 69

Taking patient to hospital, 61–67
Therapeutic community, 76–77
Therapy
activity, 38
antibiotic, 35
art, 80
dance, 81
drug, 33–34, 35, 98, 110
electroconvulsive, 34
electroshock, 34
family, 38, 42–43, 88
family care, 99, 113, 114
fashion, 83
group psychotherapy, 37–38